the river

Claus Hackenberger

Hara Publishing, Seattle

Hara Publishing Group
P.O. Box 19732
Seattle, WA 98109
(425) 775-7868

Library of Congress Number 2003110686

Manufactured in the United States
10 9 8 7 6 5 4 3 2

Hackenberger, Claus.

The river / Claus Hackenberger. -- 1st ed. --
Seattle, WA : Hara Publishing, 2003.

p. ; cm.
ISBN: 1-887542-10-8

1. Rivers--Germany--Fiction. 2. Schneidemuehl (Germany)--Fiction. 3. World War, 1939-1945-- Germany--Fiction. 4. World War, 1939-1945-- Evacuation of civilians--Germany--Fiction. 5. Biographical fiction. I. Title.

PS3608.A34 R58 2003
813.6--dc22   0310

Original Editor: Sheila Curwen
Editor in Chief: Vicki McCown
Cover Picture: Aquarelle, Gerhard Mroz
Cover Picture copied and printed with the permission of Dr. Winfried Mroz
Book Design and Production: Lisa Delaney
Illustrations: Claus Hackenberger
The artwork on p. 192 is the work of Thomas Martin Hackenberger

Also by Claus Hackenberger

A LONG WALK

In my book, *A Long Walk*, I talk about my neighbors in Germany, and how their son, "Mieschel" and I ("Paul") became friends.

Mieschel's older brother, Gerhard, at the age of sixteen, painted the picture on the cover of this book. It is a view of the Skordalina, the river that ran behind our houses in Schneidemühl.

World War II sent Gerhard to the Russian front, and in 1942, he was killed in action. His many paintings talk about the tranquility of the eastern landscape around our hometown.

In January, 1945, as the Russians approached Schneidemühl, families were given one hour to evacuate. Geela, Gerhard's sister, ripped his paintings from their frames and packed them with a few other belongings on Mieschel's sled, which they hauled to the railroad station. Hence those pictures have traveled many miles.

When I look at this one, my childhood comes alive. At the water's edge grew the cherry tree we climbed many a time. Sitting on its crooked branches, we talked about boy things and watched the carps feeding close to the surface.

This picture is a greeting from the past, from my home I never will see again.

This book is for my children, Misha, Peti, Christine, and for our Tommy who has left us already.

And, too, I wrote these lines for the sky to read, for the mountains, the wind and the sun, and for you, my river, that abundantly keeps filling my cup.

acknowledgments

Larry Barr, Candy Cullen, Dr. Edith and Dr. Winfried Mroz, and Denny Sather, thank you for your guidance, critique, and emotional support during my working on this book.

Gail Beck, my mentor, a special thanks to you for always taking care of my bird, Cheata, when I am out of town promoting my books.

Sheila Curwen, you edited my chapters, taught me how to spell, and cut my sentences to a reasonable length.

Lisa Delaney, you created the cover. You skillfully arranged and designed my book. Thank you for lending me your outstanding talents.

Sheryn Hara, you took me on again, published this second book of mine, and brought it to the marketplace. I do thank you.

Vicki McCown, my editor in chief, you further unscrambled the secret code of my precarious grammar. Like the first book, this one also would make for hard reading had it not been for your gifted touch. Thank you, Vicki!

And thanks to the many other people who tinted the ink in my pen. The river floats my sorrow, my pain, my happiness, and my peace to the sea where tides cleanse my soul. I shared love, and I hurt those who loved me. I ask them to forgive me.

contents

When *A Long Walk* reaches the river, the suspense keeps growing as does holistically the magic of Claus Hackenberger's breathtaking work. We already know him as a wonderful storyteller. Now he becomes a master storyteller captivating us in the depths of human despair and lifting us to the heights of spiritual liberation.

Here a wanderer becomes a pilgrim many times, a sojourner becomes a seeker, a storyteller often becomes an important writer exploring philosophical depths.

This book extends far but brings us back as close to reality issues as we can relate. To venture is to become an adventurer.

Just share in the adventures and I can assure you that Hackenberger is very generous—and resourceful— when sharing his.

Armin D. Lehmann
Author of
Hitler's Last Courier

Cheri

You are in my Life

Thinking of you is like dreaming

Talking to you is like saying a prayer

Holding you is like hugging our whole world

Hearing your voice is like listening to beautiful music

And loving you is like touching the ocean the earth and heaven

Part I
the river

preamble

Renton. The year is two thousand and two.

Every day, early, before the night goes to sleep, I drive my car from Renton to Southcenter, unload my bicycle, and pedal south atop the winding banks of the Green River. It is an enchanting trail alive with birds, runabout rabbits, and lots of squirrels. The tall reeds along the bank reach up to my shoulder. Hair-fine branches that look like tiny firs carry their seeds. Upstream, close to shore on the other side, geese herd their young. Large black birds pick worms from under the dewed grass around. Chirping from bushes and inside trees blends the silence with the soft running lazy river that pushes its dark waters into the big lake.

It is almost August. The morning is still brisk. The sun has yet to break over the distant Cascade Mountains to the east. Fragrant scents from wild flowers and soil spice the sleeping air. Small rabbits crisscross the path ahead. With their dark eyes on me, the little things hesitate, then, white tails up, they disappear under twisted vines weaving the border of the trail.

Around the bend ahead, a few rotting pilings left from an old bridge scratch the water's sheen. But soon the river is smooth again, peacefully floating clouds and sky towards the ocean.

The bees are still dreaming in their sweet stacks, but ants already tend to their eggs. The cantankerous black-berries are in full bloom stretching all over the sloping banks. It seems as if the myriad of white blossoms try to hide their painful thorns.

Riding along, I finished my conversation with Hail Mary. And then it happened.

There! There, the sun's wakening. Wondrous, majestic! Horizons faded into bright light. Shadows were born and thin patches of mist hovering low above the meadows turned into golden fog.

A new day had just begun. I halted and, with open arms, offered my greeting and promised to fill its hours with joy and compassion and love.

The rising fireball cast my shadow over onto the opposite riverbank. Distant and a little distorted it rode stomping up and down. It, too, wore a helmet; black, not white like mine. The wheels were not quite round, but odd ovals reached all across the river to connect with my own wheels. I let go of the handlebar and waved. Would it wave back?

The trail followed the snaking river and when I looked again, the shadow pedaled ahead of me, skimming the ground, a black blob with short pumping legs. Feeling warm, I unzipped my wind jacket and undid the top button of my flannel shirt.

For months and months, even years, had I pondered this shadow. I wondered how it could change from gray to pitch black, from long to short, from fat to thin. Did it go to bed with me, even right under my blanket? I told myself not to think about it.

But, of course, I did.

That shadow, is it a personal thing? Is it mine and mine only? It does all the things I do.

As a young boy I tried to jump over my shadow, tried to run away from it. Yes, I stepped on it, stomped it hard, though nothing harmed it. Always silent, quick and ever attached, is it maybe a dead thing? A dead thing that moves around?

I slowed down some. The trail ahead rippled. Roots of poplar trees along the riverbank had buckled the pavement in places. Like speed bumps at a grocery store parking lot, only sharper, they jarred my back and must have jarred the shadow. Coming to the end of my morning ride, I wondered if the "thing" could feel pain.

I took a good swig from my water bottle, lifted the bike onto the rack, secured it, and drove home, taking the back road by the municipal airport. Sometimes I would park there for a while and watch the small planes go and come, dreaming of my Cessna, my airplane I once had in Alaska. But this morning I went straight home.

Around noon after my visit at the post office, I fixed a sandwich and munched it while sprawled out on the garden couch in my backyard. I watched the fluttering shadow my bird, Cheata, splashed against the white aluminum siding of my house. I had built an outside cage for her with a shallow square bathtub. On sunny days I would turn on a tiny spray nozzle above the cage. Cheata loves the water.

After a short nap I took a shower. Bright sun poured through the bathroom window, and sure enough my shadow, leaning against the shower curtain lathered and rinsed right there with me. The curtain glared with water. The shadow had to be wet too, yes? But wet shadows...? I slid the curtain open. Its dark image now stretched itself over to the pastel-colored bathroom door. Quickly I went to touch it. My shadow felt drier than the sand in the desert. Was I surprised?

The next morning on the trail the shadow pedaled right in front of me. What if I talked to that thing? One hell of a thought! I felt goose bumps growing under my windbreaker. Talk to the shadow, wait for an answer? Nuts! But then, what could I lose? Nobody was around. Nobody would ever know. To even think of it, how silly can one get?

My bike trail led along the back of a warehouse that recently had shot up from nowhere. If someone were watching me, that someone might have thought I was about to commit a crime and then some. I nervously glanced in all directions. Not a soul in sight. I grabbed the handlebars like I wanted to bend them. Head down, with my chin touching my chest, I mumbled under my breath.

"Hey, you!"

"Sir?"

W h a t ?

Loving Jesus!

The dark matter had spoken. Now what?

"Did I hear you say something?"

"Well, yes. You said 'hey you,' didn't you? It would not be polite to ignore that, no?"

"You almost made me dump my bike."

"I noticed that. Frightening! Look, you'd have fallen right on top of me. You have any idea how much that would have hurt me? "

I took a deep breath.

"Easy, I've fallen many a time, never heard you scream or anything. Until now you were like a snake the Lord had forgotten to give a voice to."

"Snakes? Yuck! Sir, you make me want to curl up and puke. Don't do that to me, please!"

"I have got to see this, a puking shadow. Funny!"

Funny? Did all this really happen or had I fallen ill, mentally ill. An oncoming biker drove right over the shadow as it skimmed the blacktop of the trail.

"Now tell me, didn't that just hurt? You were worried about me falling on top of you. That man drove right over your chest."

"I like your voice, Paul. Cool. Keep talking, please."

"Don't you bait me! I am confused! I am absolutely astounded, flabbergasted..."

What? What am I?

"Paul! Paul, do you hear me? You are staring at me like you have never seen me before. Are you sick? Hey, man! Move. Blink an eye. Talk to me! What's wrong? Did I say something you didn't like?"

"How do you know my name?"

"A no-brainer. You really surprise me. When you saw daylight for the first time and let out your first yell— ever since then I've been right there with you. And when your father and mother held your little head over that baptismal water basin, and the priest for the first time called you Paul—man, I heard that too."

This shadow has a memory?

"How can you have a memory, when I see no real head you could store all this in?"

"I am very complex. Yes. You planet dwellers are some breed! Ha, I..."

"Let it go for a while, okay? Where were we? Oh yeah, you answered me. Wow! Sixty-five years have gone by without my having the slightest clue that my shadow can talk. Do you hear what I'm saying?"

"Not my fault, sir. No shadow ever is allowed to speak unless spoken to by its master. You should have tried earlier to catch my attention. I've been ready for a long time."

"You talk a good line. In other words you would have kept silent forever had I not said 'hi' to you?"

"That's it. Yes. I would have been buried with you without ever having uttered one single word. But, don't disturb this beautiful moment with banalities!"

"Hold that thought. Are you telling me that they will bury you with me, and in the same coffin?"

"Yes, we are around no longer than our host is. It's hard to explain. You people die. We don't, we just fade away in the dark."

"Huh?"

"Are you teasing me? Think, six feet under, it's dark down there. Yes, you'll be glowing for a while, but then after that, you…"

"Stop that talk! It makes me shiver. I mean…"

"Gee, you don't care. You don't give a damn. I knew it! And I always thought of you as such a loving person."

"Never mind that right now. More important, tell me, when you talk, can other people hear you?"

"Why? Do you worry?"

"Just answer the question."

I began to be concerned where this discussion could be leading. Testing, I kept silent for a couple of miles. It rode with me in silence. Several more bikers ran right over its neck. I started to feel squeezed. Unconsciously, I reached for my throat to check for tire marks. I felt relieved when I didn't feel any. The shadow kept silent.

I turned around at the four-mile mark and realized that this "thing" had been with me even when life stacked up those ugly moments—when I was not being faithful to my women or staggering about in drunkenness or calling 900 numbers in the middle of the night… Wow! Would it remember all of those bad events I had involved myself in?

Oh my God!

"Paul—may I call you 'Paul'?"

"You got manners, good. 'Paul' is okay, of course."

"Something is bothering me. We need to talk about it, yes?"

I felt it coming.

"I always have admired you. Even during the war when you shot down Allied airplanes and then later during all the years in those French slave labor camps, I stood by you."

"What's your point?"

"Well, there is this past of yours. I…"

"Why does my past bother you? Again, what is your point?"

But I did not wait for the answer and looked the other way. I was done with what had been. Why did this black "thing" bug me with it? Did it want to make me feel guilty all over again? I have news for it, I have forgiven myself and I have forgiven the people who hurt me. I learned this to be the only way to get well, to become free, and to have peace in me.

I cannot change the past, no matter how much I might like to. And, to be honest I do not know what tomorrow will bring. So, if I am serious about life, now is the moment I must live my life, reach out, share, give, love, and make amends. Now and only now!

The river disappeared behind a bend, and the shadow stretched all the way over to the other bank. I hollered.

"Okay, come closer. Over here! We'll talk."

The trail curved again. The black thing slipped right under me, and I kept driving on it.

"Doesn't that hurt you? A while back you said if I'd fallen on you, it would have been very painful. No?"

"I lied."

"You what? You puke and you lie? What else is there that will surprise me?"

"I'll explain all that later..."

"That is if I ever give you another chance to talk to me."

"Okay, okay."

"One more time, please tell me, do other people hear you talk? Yes or no? No lying about that. Do you understand?"

"Relax! Nobody hears me say anything. That is the truth. But think, Paul, people might wonder how come you are talking to yourself. Now, you need to know that I don't like this arrangement, but..."

I shook my head. The shadow kept on talking.

"Let's get back to our discussion. I never had a chance to mention how hard you made it to live with you through all those bad scenes you created. Many times I really wanted to fade away forever. Too often I…"

"Can't we leave those things for later? I don't have a clue yet about you. What are you made of? You need to tell me about yourself. Are you male or female? Did they give you a name?"

"Yes. 'Paul,' that is my name, and I am an 'it.'"

"Neutered? Jesus!"

"No, not 'Jesus.' 'Paul.'"

"Smart ass. 'Paul'? That is absurd. That's my name!"

"I don't care, any name will do. You just have to register me anew."

"You are making this up. Yes?"

The spiked pavement of the trail came in sight again. I had to come up with a name. Why did I ever start this?

Entering my house I turned off the ADT alarm and stored the bicycle. From my workshop I called my girlfriend.

"Cheataaaa?" (Her name is pronounced as "Keetah.")

"Wwraahhh-raa raa."

She had been waiting for me, and the moment I entered my kitchen, she stretched to almost twice her size and chirped. With her wings low and her beak pointing straight to heaven, I patted her gently, asked her about her day, and gave her a kiss right on the beak. Then I drank the rest of the coffee left over from the morning. Now cold, it tasted flat, not good. But I did not have the heart to pour this expensive brown stuff down the drain.

Cheata's "place" needed cleaning. It's one of my morning chores that help me to get my neurons firing the way they are supposed to. She lives in the garden window above the kitchen counter, sharing a large space with some of my cactus plants. No cage limits her freedom. From the center of a round Plexiglas bowl, partially filled with dry shredded corncobs, grows a tall maple wood branch. It has a sharp bend at the top and looks like an upside-down golf club. I had carved it into a perch.

She has a terrific view of the backyard. She watches the neighbor's dog or any passing cat wondering how this blue bird behind the glass could be had. For some reason she does not like squirrels. She screams when these half-rats come and screw up the flower boxes blooming on my porch.

A name! I needed to come up with a name for this "it" thing. Or should I forget the whole affair? But I could not resist digging the hole a little deeper. "Shat" or just "it"?

Tomorrow.

I did not sleep well that night and got up before five. While tying my Nikes I continued to think about this shadow thing.

Angling my bike through the narrow passage leading from the workshop to the front door, I bumped into a picture hanging on the wall. It came loose from its nail. The frame did not survive and neither did the glass. The photo showed Toi and me holding hands. We had met on a beautiful island in the South China Sea, many, many years ago. I remember we were very happy. She allowed me to love her the way I thought love should be shared. But then I started to drink again. Undoubtedly, Shat would bring this up sometime soon.

Biking again a few days later a shy morning breeze from the south blew against me. I never liked that wind. It made it so much harder for me to bike against it. Gray air from a gray sky covered the trail. I could not make out a distinct outline of Shat. I had to really strain my eyes to find the fuzzy line between gray and gray.

"Hey, Shat!"

"Excuse me. 'Shat'? 'Shat'? Paul, that sounds like a dressed up s-word. No! No! Please no."

"You have a dirty mind?"

"Well, mine is like yours, sort of, though I never use the words you let go when you are mad."

"Not true. I never am mad anymore. Besides 'Shat' will have five letters if we add another 't,' yes? By the way, I hardly can see you."

"If you think you are funny, you're not. You are changing the subject. Let's talk about my name, okay?"

"Well, how about 'it'?"

"Never! 'It' reminds me of Stephen King's horror stories. You are being rude, sarcastic, and really not very nice at all. Too bad I just have to take it. We shadows…"

"Sorry. You have feelings too? That's a new one on me. Are you lying again? How does 'Shatty' grab you? Six letters. Better?"

The shadow giggled. I never to this point had ever seen or heard a shadow giggle. I swear!

"Man, you humans are something else. Yeah, I'll try getting used to being 'Shatty.' Give me some time, will you, please?"

I thought that went pretty well, though I still couldn't believe all this; my shadow talked, I heard it giggle. I began to worry about me, just a little.

Back at home Cheata tilted her head, looking at me with one eye. A bright sun reached through my sliding glass door and leaned my Shatty dark against the almond-colored refrigerator door. Was she wondering about that?

"Shatty, have you ever met Cheata's shadow?"

"Paul, do you call it perhaps 'Birdie'? Ha, gotcha!"

Shatty had a sense of humor, another piece not fitting the puzzle.

"Why don't you ask Cheata yourself?"

"Paul, this is a sensitive subject. You see, our society is built around a strict class system. Yes, it's a power structure."

"Hold it. A while back on the bike trail I asked you to not ever pull my leg. Right now you are not only doing that, worse, you are snowing me. No more lying boy, or I will not talk with you ever again."

"I am not a boy and I am not lying. I promise, seriously. Look, billions of people have billions of shadows. Living things, animals, trees, and bushes have shadows. Lifeless things that move around like clouds, cars, and airplanes have shadows also. And then there are the shadows of dead things that never move at all. Think of mountains, a house or just a plain old rock."

"So? Big deal. What's that got to do with you talking to Cheata?"

"Paul, please, let me finish. Shadows that can communicate with their hosts stand on the top rung of the ladder. Shadows of my class are not allowed—and never would try—to associate with the ones belonging to animals or dead things. You need to understand, those shadows are never spoken to and therefore…"

"You are not arrogant, huh? All of you are made of the same stuff—actually, of photons that cannot pass through me, and such do not exist for you at all. So it's probably more accurate to say that all of you are made of the same non-stuff, yes? You better be nice to Cheata's shadow."

"Jeez, you are a real funny guy. 'I am made of things that aren't there, do not exist.' That hurts, Paul, that hurts. Look at you. You are made of a few carbon atoms mixed with red water. How does that fit?"

"It works, doesn't it?"

No answer. Shatty probably made a face saying, "So?" But it kept talking.

"Why do we have to be stuck with one host for all eternity, jerk or saint?"

"Poor baby! Would you understand if I told you? Say, who is changing the subject now?"

"So you went to school on being an arse, yes? You were always so pissed when your father gave you such an answer like 'You would not understand...' 'You're too young yet...' blah blah blah. "

"I'm sorry. I just don't understand how nothingness can have feelings, have a hierarchy, be arrogant, yet never can move around on its own free will. Tell me."

"By golly, sure glad I am not an earthling. Jesus, Paul you are confused. You wonder about all this and..."

"Do you know Him, Jesus?"

"Why?"

"Can you ever give me a straight answer, no?"

"Just listen to your questions. They are so... but I'm not going there right now. Of course I know Him. I got baptized at the same time you did. You dense or something?"

What a tongue this black thing dares.

"Shatty, that borders on being disrespectful to your master."

A religious shadow! What else don't I know about this character? I cut Shatty off by looking the other way. I needed only to do that and keep quiet to get a handle on the situation. Not very polite, but it worked. I felt at ease.

My promotional trip through Oregon had been a success. The booksellers had responded cordially.

"You know you could have at least blinked at me once in a while. There was plenty of sun around, and I really tried to show off for you. But no, you didn't even..."

"Shatty, you were right there with me."

"You never will get it. No."

"Peace?"

"I heard you telling people that you are working on your second book. Nice to know."

"Guy, enough. I am sitting right on you when I type my chapters. Don't you know?"

"I left something out. We shadows cannot read."

"No small wonder. All along I searched where your eyes possibly could be. But you have none. You need none. I am doing the seeing for you, right?"

"Wonderful, your deductions are brilliant. Who ever taught you to think... Oh, skip it! What's in your new book?"

"Shatty, I will read it to you once it is on the market."

"Your career, your marriages, your airplane, your women, your boozing, that book is going to be fatter than a Webster's dictionary."

"Shatty, you know how to hurt a guy. Who taught you that?"

"'Member the apple that did not fall far from the tree it had been born on?"

"Well, at least it happened to be a smart branch you fell off from. Yes, I promise, I will write about all those things as I remember them happening. So don't you worry, okay?"

"Seriously, Paul, I am very sad. You will be writing on that new book, and it will take all of your time. You know, it is so beautiful to ride up and down the river with you."

"Of course, Shatty. We are a good team, and I might need your help whenever my memory wants to play hide and seek with my life. Yes, we need one another."

"Paul, sorry, but shadows cannot cry. You don't have to go so deep."

Right, how could Shatty cry without having eyes?

"Shatty, will I ever really know who you are?"

1

the university

A cold November wind pitched drizzling rain against my flimsy overcoat. Still dark, the gaslights along the sidewalk flickered from the top of their ornamental iron posts. Small drops danced in the bluish light that glittered them into flocks of sparkling diamonds.

I stood at the curb of the narrow street in Ansbach, a little up from Mr. Holzmann's house. For nine months, I had walked here on my way to and from school.

The class of 1948 had graduated the day before. Barely a year had passed since I had come here to attend this special curriculum at the Stein Gymnasium. The seminar was intended to help us young World War II prisoners to plug the large holes in our education, and to somehow shuffle us back into the new society of a destroyed country, a nation run over by death.

And now, on this morning in November, 1948, all of those twenty-one students were leaving this little town in Germany to begin elsewhere, somehow, a new life.

Lost, sad, and very lonely, I thought of my options. I had no one to go home to. No one waited for me. The bedroom I had rented from the Holzmann family had been my first safe place since 1943, the year I had left my hometown Schneidemühl.

Just a few minutes before, Else and Felix Holzmann had hugged me goodbye. The night before their son, Ludwig, had come to my room sobbing.

"Will I ever see you again? Why don't you find a job around here? I will miss your talking about space and time and eternity... I... I wish you would be my brother..."

"Ludwig, time goes on. You are on your way to become a man. Keep on reading about those galaxies we traveled together, and one day, maybe, we'll meet again, wiser and older..."

"I don't want you to leave! It is the way you speak about things, the pictures you use to make me understand. How will I do without you?"

"I will miss you too, all of you, and in so many ways. Your mother's boiled potatoes and her homemade sausage I will remember for time to come. Your father, I know he at first was worried about me living in his house. But after we got acquainted, I felt he accepted me. And yes, I will miss him too... All of you have given me so much and have helped me to become free again. It is all right for you to cry, Ludwig. Tears need to be wept. My mother used to say, 'Wherever a tear falls to the ground, a flower will sprout.'"

I led him to the door.

"Remember now, let's not look back. Tomorrow is a new day that needs us and we better be there to do our work. Goodbye, Ludwig."

I closed the door and sat down on that squeaky chair by the small table near the window and cried.

How this life of mine would unfold I wondered, and where would it take me.

I stood at an on-ramp to the turnpike heading north. I had decided to hitchhike in this direction to wherever one of those speeding cars would take me. A gentleman, probably in his sixties, stopped, looked at me, and then asked me to throw my suitcase on the back seat. I took him to be a business man. He asked where I came from and where I was going. I told him about the seminar and that I had no place to go to.

"So, please, let me off any time you have arrived at your destination."

"No parents, not a friend anywhere?"

"My parents and my younger sister fled from the Russians and now live in Bavaria. It's a small village, nothing going on there. They all live in one room in the attic above the milking stable. I went to see them after my escape. We could not bridge the time. I could not stay with them..."

"You are too young for all this to happen to you."

He offered me an American cigarette, a Camel, and with his eyes on the road, not me, he kept talking.

"I did not have it that bad at all. My father owned a shoe factory. When Hitler outfitted his new army, we

switched to making military boots. We must have produced millions of those Soldaten Stiefeln. It saved my
father and me from going to war. Sure, we had our share
of terrible nights in Mannheim's air-raid shelters. They
really bombed our town. Times were tough, but we always had money to get things on the black market."

The cigarette bud burned my thumb, leaving hardly
anything to stub out in that fancy dashboard ashtray. I
wished he'd told me all that in a less arrogant tone. At
that time I harbored uncomfortable feelings towards those
who I felt had not quite done their share. I declined his
offer to stay at his home in Mannheim where he would
help me find a job, instead asking politely for him to
drop me off at the Heidelberg exit.

"No, thank you, sir. I know of a girl there," I lied.

I took the tram to Mannheim where a friend from
Ansbach had told me his parents were living. I found
them without much trouble, and they helped me rent a
place in a remodeled air-raid shelter. The city did not
charge much for those bug-infested holes in the wall. A
regular apartment was out of the question. They had long
waiting lists for families only, none for single people. I
had a little money left from my scrap-burning job, so I
signed up. I would live there for almost a year.

Not at all sure of myself, I debated the consequences
and decided to become an engineer. The University in
Darmstadt rejected my first application. The note read:

"... We accept only students with a high school diploma and who also have graduated from an apprenticeship course of a kind..."

I searched for a firm where I could join such a program and found a large construction company, Guen & Bilfinger, which took me on as an apprentice. I would learn to be a mechanic. That suited me well, since I had worked as one in the French slave labor camp. The apprenticeship council made me a good deal. My time as a welder in the coal mine's repair shop would go towards the required three-year apprentice term. I also would be paid the same as if I were in the third year of the program. They tested me frequently, and after nine months let me take the exam. Like any other test I ever have taken, I passed it with a C.

The clerk at the University in Darmstadt accepted my papers and told me to be back in two weeks to take the test. It would take two days of answering questions, both in writing and in an interview.

In late 1948, prisons and slave labor camps had opened their gates, and homecoming prisoners flooded educational institutions. Some six hundred would come to Darmstadt to take the tests at that acknowledged and prestigious university, Germany's MIT.

The results would determine the basic level of knowledge required to matriculate. Should I be accepted, and I did not detect a glimmer of compassion in their letter, the first semester would start in November, 1949. I would not be charged tuition for the first semester since I had been a prisoner of war.

During my time in Mannheim I had acquired a secondhand bicycle that looked and rode more like a fourth-hand one. I left on it at noon the day before the tests. I had no money for a train ticket. It took me a little over five hours pedaling along the Odenwälder Weinstrasse. Cold and rainy wind blew against me as I passed by the small towns of Heidenheim and Bensheim. I worried about the tires of my bike. If one would go flat, plan "B" did not exist. I had on me the cash equivalent of three dollars. I knew, not showing up would postpone my engineering endeavor for at least a full year, maybe forever.

It had gotten dark. Finally in the distance I saw the blinking street lights of Mühlthal, a small village south of Darmstadt. I felt good to be close to the end of my trip. My hands were numb and I had begun to shiver. An ugly wind pitched ice-cold raindrops straight into my face. It felt like the blowing snow during my long walk into freedom two years earlier. Life sure had not become much easier. Uncertainty lingered. Will I make it? This question surfaced anew many times over. During my years in those slave labor camps I only had to answer one question. Do I want to live? Not a number of answers there to choose from. My answer took just three letters: "y-e-s." And during those barbed-wire years I had spoken this "yes" so many times, it had become my prayer.

It took me a while to find the house where my friend Otto and his wife Sandy lived with her parents. The door opened to reveal an attractive young woman.

"Oh my God! Paul, you are wet all the way through! Your hands are blue. Man, you must be exhausted. Come on in quick, come."

I had never seen Sandy, though Otto had told me about her beauty. He had been right. I guessed her to be around six-foot, as tall as I stood. She carried herself with the certain elegance of a well-brought-up young lady. I liked her right away. She wore a beige sweater that matched her brown flannel skirt. No jewelry hung anywhere from her, except she wore a small dressy watch on her right wrist. No fancy fragrance drifted about her.

"Hello, Sandy! My God, is it ever good to see you. Let me take off my shoes. They are full of water. It squishes out from under my toes every time I take a step."

Where the rain had not gotten to, passing cars had taken care of it. Wet all the way through to my bones, I stepped under the overhang above the front door.

"Look, even the pockets of my "water-tight" wind-breaker are bulging with water."

She led me upstairs to the small room they called their home.

In 1946, Otto and I had met at the French camp in Merlebach, where we shared Barrack #9, our home at the coal mine. Before I escaped at Christmas in 1947, he had given me his home address which I had sewn into the collar of my shirt. I had written to his sweetheart,

Sandy, after I arrived in Ansbach, telling her that all was well with Otto. The French government released Otto with the rest of the prisoners of war late in 1948. Otto found me later while I was working in Mannheim on my apprenticeship.

"I'll help you, Paul. I have a good job with my uncle who is in the cookie/chocolate/wine sales business."

Sandy's room, warm and cozy made me feel safe. A worn couch covered one wall. The narrow gable window was dressed with a yellow curtain, a light-brown valance tried to hide the rod. Four oaken chairs kind of leaned against the edge of the small dining table in the middle of the room. A blue-and-white wax tablecloth covered its worn top. The lamp hanging from the ceiling right above the table needed a new shade. The smell of stew and onions snuck up the stairs and filled the place.

"Sandy, thank you, thank you! How could I possibly do tomorrow without your help?"

"Let's not talk about that now. Otto will be home later. He said he would drive you to the U in the morning. Don't worry about your bike. Nobody will take that. Otto and I thought that you also should stay here tomorrow night, yes?"

I gave Sandy a long, long hug.

"Jeez, Paul! Now I'm wet too. Here, try on those pants. They are Otto's. I hope they fit. If not, my mother downstairs will hem them."

Wrapped in a blanket, I sat on the couch, still shivering. She poured hot water into a washbowl. It reminded me of my "lavatory" in Ansbach.

"Come, warm your icy hands. Otto told me to take good care of you. You might know, he likes you a lot. Here, take this. It is from both of us."

She pushed it into my right hand. I looked and saw 50 Deutschmarks. For that money I could buy a lot of train tickets.

"No, no, it's okay. We want you to have that, please take it. You will need it."

I got a little moist around my eyes.

The hot water changed the blue of my hands into a deep red. Sandy threw one of Otto's shirts and a pair of woolen socks at me.

The pants were a little long, but they would do if I kept pulling them up. Homemade split pea soup! Sandy's mother, Frau Gertz, brought it up. The stairs creaked with every step she took.

"Paul, please, meet my mother. We call her by her last name, just Gertz. She likes it that way."

"Hello, Frau Gertz—okay, yes—hello, Gertz. You all are so kind. I don't know how I can ever thank you." "You are Otto's friend, Paul, and that means a lot to all of us. I heard about you and he pulling off some of those risky things at that slave shop you worked in. It gives me the willies every time I think of it. Well, come and have some of that soup, it will warm you. We'll eat dinner when Otto gets home."

The couch moaned a little as I sat down. That hot soup tasted terrific and the tremors in my body finally ceased to shake me. My hands tingled and my lower jaw no longer jammed into my upper teeth. And then dark surrounded me.

Otto had to shake me.

"Hey man, what do you think this place is? A hotel? Wake up! You can't sleep all night sitting on this here couch. Sandy's mother has a bed for you downstairs."

I strained to remember where I was.

"Otto, man, is it ever good to see you! Thank you for letting me stay here. Sandy gave me dry clothes. They all belong to you, and if you would not have grown so tall, they would fit perfectly. Thank you anyway."

Sandy added, "Otto, he got here wetter than a fish…"

"I know it's after nine already, and you need a good night of sleep, but let's have a glass of wine before we go to bed. Sandy, sweetheart, get the bottle for special occasions. Paul, we need to celebrate…"

"You think we might want to wait until I am accepted?"

"Too late by then! Between your studying and earning a living at night, I am afraid we will not see much of you."

"How can you be so sure I am going to make it? I'm not. I am very uncertain, very. I hear those tests are tough. And I never have I been good with crossword puzzles. You know my gears up here are still not mashing right."

"Hey, guy, you made it to here. You will make it tomorrow and all the days thereafter. Paul, I know you.

Remember Barrack #9? I often wondered where those rabbits came from you constantly were pulling out from under your hat. You did not fool me then, you don't fool me now. Crank it up and run! That's an order! Here's to you and to all of us!"

The wine, a Riesling from a nearby vineyard's sacred golden grapes, renewed a friendship that began one night in the French coal mine camp back, in the corner when Knute and Martin and Otto had offered me my first shot of Pernod. How much time had passed by since! Sandy gave me a kiss.

"It's okay, you'll make it all right, we all will. Now let's hit the hay. "

The quietness in the huge lecture hall, a half-round arena, stunned me. The ceiling and walls showed discolorations. Heavy rains had leaked through the roof. The university buildings had suffered severely during the Allied bombing raids. Whole city blocks were waiting in rubble, still bearing witness to the awesome destruction of human shelter and life, square miles of broken bricks stacked eight feet high.

Some hundred young men hunched uncomfortably on the benches that looked like pews except for the missing kneeling boards. The further away from the hall's center, the higher up the students were sitting. Every other row remained empty for the staff to pass through and to observe our progress. I found a seat halfway up the slope right before the professor entered, dragging behind a whirlwind of assistants dressed in white, freshly ironed doctor coats. It got quieter yet.

The man one over from me whispered that he wanted to leave and pursue the carpenter career he had started with his apprenticeship. I, too, felt insecure...

Hail Mary, Hail Mary, really, I am so afraid. I had not prayed to her for a while. Would she listen now?

The cloaked men stationed themselves at each end of the rows.

"Meine Herren! Gentlemen, you are at the Technical University in Darmstadt. Your applications have been reviewed. You are the chosen ones we invited to take this test. Your answers must be complete. We expect you to be correct 90 percent of the time. Good luck."

Pause.

Welcome?

Ninety percent?

The professor's voice sounded cold, sharp like a razor blade, not inviting, not encouraging at all. I wondered where he had been during the war.

"You have been told not all of you will be able to attend the coming 1949 winter semester. We have only sixty-five openings. Within a few days we will let you know whether you are in or out.

"One more item, please. No communication with your neighbor is permitted. If my assistants notice that you fail to observe this rule, we will see to it that you never again will be asked to come back. Gentlemen, do we understand each other?"

Silent nodding conveyed concurrence. The white army handed out the test sheets.

I had brought two pencils, one with an eraser at one end. My hands were clam and cold. I pulled one from the breast pocket of Otto's shirt and chuckled, thinking of what he had said about the rabbits under my hat.

Again, I asked myself whether I was doing the right thing. If I passed those tests and were admitted, my semester grades would have to be in the three-point-or-better range in order for me to get help with the tuition. It would be very hard for me, the C-average student, to achieve that. I had no money. I'd have to get a job and a room in this town. The odds seemed to stack up against me. Yet I decided to stay and take the test.

"Name, date of birth, ID number, home address. Please write clearly so we can read it"

That jarred me back to reality but fast. My handwriting did not look any better than that of third-graders. The "inspectors" recommended that we first read all the questions.

"Do the ones you feel comfortable with, and then try the other ones. Take your time; you have eight hours today and six tomorrow."

One hundred questions in fourteen hours? Wow!

"This is bad!"

I looked to my neighbor on my right. His face had turned ashen, and he kept shaking his head in slow motion. Well, at least others were scared too.

I started to read.

>*Trees sprouting from a slope grow straight up. What makes them do that? Ice floats in water. Do you know why? What is light made of? Falling stars have a bright tail. Can you explain? What is the square root of minus 3?*

And there were other ones.

>*You are boiling water. Does a lid on the kettle shorten the time to boiling, or does it come to boil faster without a lid? Explain why.*

>*Gauge the diameter of a full moon by using your index finger and thumb. How many millimeters are they apart? What is missing in this question?*

>*Give five reasons why you want to study engineering. Give five more reasons why you want to do that at this university.*

>*Why does a rainbow never touch the ground, or does it?*

>*Given the equation 5+5=10, how many times can it be expressed differently?*

And on and on and on! We had an hour for lunch. I went to the Mensa, the university's cafeteria, and with some of Sandy's money I bought a cup of potato soup. I felt worn out already. Still to come that afternoon were questions pertaining to health, history, physics, and chemistry. When I returned to the arena I saw holes in the rows that had looked so overcrowded this morning.

At five in the afternoon we were dismissed.

I slid into Otto's maroon-colored Mercedes, buried my head in my hands, and began to laugh—loud, and louder, hysterically.

"Otto, who in all hell do I think I am?"

In between my gulping for air, Otto learned about the 90 percent completion requirement.

"No way will I make it! Otto, no way! Do you hear me, man? I…"

"Did you answer all the questions?"

"Not all, about sixty. Man, did I guess up a storm! Right now I don't even think I'm going in tomorrow."

"Partner, you shut up this very moment. You're pissing me off!"

I remembered the hot discussions the four of us had at times in Barrack #9. Otto had a quick temper. His face would distort ever so slightly and his lower lip would quiver, just like right now.

"You son of a bitch, I don't want to hear this. Did you leave your gut in France? Man, what happened? You're not, in any way, the guy I used to know."

Otto started to breathe heavy. His hands were grabbing that steering wheel like he wanted to rip it off its column. We were speeding over 150 km an hour along a dark, two-lane country road. The trees on both sides turned into solid green walls. The high-beam headlights chased down an endless tunnel.

"Shit, Paul, shall I drive you to the railroad station, buy you a ticket to Mannheim, and kick your ass onto that train? Want me to? I'll do it, just say so!"

"Otto! Otto, knock it off!" I screamed at him. His face twitched, and the Merc kept squealing around the bends. I never had seen him this angry. "This here does not have anything to do with guts. It has to do with having to come up with answers to questions about things I never knew existed."

Silence, only the diesel engine roared, filling this empty moment.

"I'm sorry I lost it."

And turning to me, this gentle otto-betzler-face broke into a disarming grin, a grin no one ever could resist, a grin that makes one feel good, a grin I never will forget. He slowed down, stopped the car and we hugged each other.

"You see, Paul, it's not only you, I am worried too. You are my guy, my friend, my brother. I want you to succeed. I…"

"Thank you, Otto. I know you are my friend, and I know all of you worry about me. During the orals tomorrow I might have a chance to change my odds."

"Yeah, see."

He reached for my hand. I squeezed his fingers hard and I held them for a while.

Gertz had cooked a big meal. Pork roast with mashed potatoes and thick brown gravy. I took a little sauerkraut and a boiled onion with it. Nobody seemed to mind my overloaded plate. Sandy had lit some candles, adding to the romance of this very peaceful occasion.

We ate, drank wine, laughed, and after a slice of blueberry pie, we discussed a few of those questions. Mr. Gertz got hooked on the "moon thing." He had been in America for a while, in Chicago, and considered himself a well-traveled man. As years went by, I would find him to be an all-around hell of a guy. He would tell me about the greatness and the freedom that lived in America. He sported a grayish, short-clipped mustache and always wore sweaters of various pastel colors. I don't think I ever saw him wearing a jacket. His wrinkled face framed a pair of gentle eyes that blinked with love.

"I think, I know what is missing. What did you say?"

"Well, let's hear your take, Mr. Gertz."

"Okay, I think a fixed distance between your eye and your gauging fingers should have been specified."

"Believe it or not, I said that too. Maybe I'm not so dumb after all."

Frau Gertz came to sit next to me on the couch. She came close and whispered, "Paul, believe me, you're not dumb."

That made me blush. Sandy wanted to know what my answer had been regarding this infinite radius of a circle.

Question: "What happens to a circle when its radius reaches infinity?"

Otto grinned.

"Berck, now that's easy for you. No? Einstein and all that stuff, right down your alley, huh?"

The man from Chicago didn't say a thing. Gertz's long knitting needles clicked as the shawl imperceptibly grew from under her hands. Otto kept grinning. Sandy washing dishes, turned.

"If the radius goes to infinity, so does the curvature. It's no longer a circle. It has become a straight line. That's all there is to it. True?"

"Close, Sandy. Infinity does not change things; it just stretches them beyond our imagination. That means in this case that a curve always will stay a curve, even in infinity. It will almost become a straight line, almost."

One more toast. Otto gave me a hug then the night took us all.

"Sleep well. I love you, Berck."

I did make it! I did pass the test! Unbelievable! Hail Mary had listened, yes. Out of six hundred applicants, I slipped under the wire as the last one of the sixty-five they were admitting.

My first semester began in November, 1949. It took me twelve semesters, six years of hard labor, to get my masters degrees in structural, civil, and mechanical engineering. During the first semester I just sat there, wrote down a bunch of stuff, missing the essence of the lesson. To get my brain cranking again after all those years of only thinking about food and how to make it through the next hour proved to be quite the job. But I was not alone, and that helped me survive the many days of despair.

My daily seminars started at eight in the morning. It took most of the day to attend all of them, and I had always heavy homework to do. My fuzzy concept of integral equations and the like made me work twice as hard as some of the others in my class. To support myself I got a job working as a waiter in a well-known restaurant in Darmstadt. I did that four nights a week, from 6 PM to midnight. I had rented a room in nearby Eberbach, a small suburb of Darmstadt, about twenty tram-minutes away from the university. I never had enough money to heat the place, and during the winter my feather bed sometimes iced up around my nose. During later years at the university, I literally lived in my study hall and went home to my apartment to change clothes once in a while. Nearly all of us scraped the bottom every day to come up with a mark or two to pay for a meager meal, usually a chunk of salted pork and week-old dry bread.

Sandy and Otto helped me in so many ways to survive these hard years. They often invited me to eat with them, put money in my pocket, and helped me up when I had my down days. There were many times when I thought I no longer could hang in there.

I had hoped the memory of the horrible hours in the prison camp would recede. It did not happen. All during the first years in Darmstadt I had horrifying dreams that mauled my short nights. Soldiers would storm into my room. Soldiers without heads stripped me naked and wrapped my body in a blanket made of barbed wire. There were other prisoners, yet I could not talk to or touch anybody during this endless trip to the coal mine camp in Merlebach. All the barracks had disappeared. I saw only graves and so many of them. Deep from beneath the earth, horrifying, woeful, terribly awful screams broke the surface, scaring me. The headless soldiers pushed me towards an open pit filled with flames that begged me to touch them. I heard the voices of men and friends who had succumbed in that infamous American hunger camp, Kreuznach. My own screaming would wake me up, shaking and bathed in sweat. Often I would find myself curled up on the floor in some corner of my room. I had many of those dreams, all were so very real.

Even during the day I saw the corpses I had stepped over. I kept hearing the screams of burning people during that bombing inferno in Stettin. This past did not want to leave me and it made me think of death and destruction.

I am reading from my logbook, Darmstadt, November, 1950:

> *Maybe the barren trees, the cold autumn wind, the low, heavy clouds do this to me. I do not know why I think of death at times like these. The wet ground feels frosty. Wilted leaves are rotting everywhere. Year after year, between harvest time and winter snow, my thoughts torture me.*
>
> *My soul hurts.*

Über den Tod

Almost scared am I when I walk through the forest. Those naked, skeleton branches remind me that life only lasts for a short while. Everything in the end turns to dust. The sapless twigs chafing in the blowing rain frighten my walk.

I can not help it.

How much longer will I have? My time, when will it be called? With a sudden blow it comes to me. Inescapably I will be with these wet leaves some day, be part of them. I need to prepare so I can accept this enormous event, the blink in time when my answers must turn to yes.

They will have a white paper shirt for me then. Someone will arrange my stiff hands. They will light candles trying to stretch the moment already past. The hole has been measured. I can hear the shovel's click as it strikes small rocks in the soil. The hourglass is running on air, not a crumb of sand left to fall through the orifice. Even if someone tried to turn it over one more time, the crystals would no longer count my time. Graves will be all around me. Yet I will shiver alone towards the day promised that all would rise again.

Why do I fear?

It has not been that long ago when I saw the black hooded shadow kill, relentlessly, arbitrarily, and at random. These times were so very grueling, terribly awesome, and so very destructive. Man had hired death. Death took over and hired mankind.

Unforgiving.

*Even those who did the killing were slaugh-
tered, twisted, and shredded. I still do and I will
forever hear the swishing the hatchet made as it
sliced through mangled masses of human beings.
Women and children dug deep ditches. Others
threw in the empty frames, torsos without white
paper shirts, without coffins, without candles, without prayers. Just that dull thump coming up from
the ditch as the bodies bounced off one another.*

Why am I afraid?

*How will I die? Will they torture me, use me
as their living candle? Will they bury me alive?
Will they drag me behind their jeep till I lose my
limbs, drown me, or cut me open?*

*Often I feel that I should hurry with the things
I still want to do. My leaving, the world will not
notice. My neighbors soon will forget.*

*But for me it will be the essence of my life. No
one else will be there but God. I wish, though,
He would tell me before it's time to go.*

I also began to argue a lot with God. Raised a Catholic, I had been told that the Lord fixes everything that is
broken. The priest in the confessional would forgive me
if I felt sorry. His grace would always be there to make
me whole again.

Who are you God? Your shepherds reign by guilt and
punishment. But why should I live in fear of You, when
Your grace is boundless? Someone invented hell. Maybe

I should be afraid. You allowed those soldiers to nail Your Son to that cross. Why is He still hanging from it? Why? Is it to remind us how cruel You can be? If You do this to Your Son, what might You do to me?

Sometimes my thoughts bordered on heresy.

I am who I am, what I am. Not a thing about me is halfway. When I am greedy, I do it well. Envy and jealousy, I am very good at. In rage, I lose all sight, and hardly find a way to repent. My name could be "Unrest." Sometimes I swear at life. I am very good at all those things.

Tell me, why is it so hard for me to accept Your mightiness? Why don't I have a talent for that? Why do I doubt that You bring peace, love? Why can I not see that You conquered evil, hate, deceit? Why am I not good at that?

Why did You drive them from your garden? I've never met Adam. Why did You tempt him, make him fail? You knew he would. He made love to Eve. What did You expect? You made Eve and him to do just that! So why should I care about their "sin"?

Something went wrong? Could that happen to You? No. Is it a flaw in Your master plan?

And now you want me to fix it? That, I refuse to believe!

Is it so much fun for You to see me break? Do You enjoy watching me grapple for the grace they say You are?

My darkness dims Your light. Storms in my soul distort Your image. Why is it so very hard for me to find You, and talk to You? Lord, what is it with me, I do not know who You are, and yet I pray to You?

My years in Darmstadt were witness to my first writings, in both prose and poetry. I also began to paint flowers, roses, and landscapes. I painted souls escaping from the bomb craters of that so horrible war. Everything I drew or painted, I did in black, in charcoal, pencil, or black chalk.

During my third semester in January of 1951, I married Rita. We rented a room in Heidenheim, a small town leaning against the foothills of the Odenwälder Mountains, halfway between Darmstadt and Mannheim. Times were tough, but Frau Schutzl, our landlord, helped

out wherever she could. The "chamber" she rented to us was not much larger than ten by twelve. The wooden floor had run out of paint some time ago. Its boards were slightly warped, enough to keep the table wiggling no matter how I shimmed its legs. The wallpaper, yellowish, frayed in places, talked of times neither one of us could remember. I cannot think of what the ceiling looked like, though it hung low enough that I could reach it by standing on my toes. The only window opened to the north and the Horst Heinemann Strasse below. Never had this place seen any sunshine.

I don't recall where we got the furniture from, but we moved in with a narrow mattress, a miniature table with two beaten-up chairs, and a portable closet. In the corner, near the door, stood an old-fashioned coal stove. On cold days it heated the room and gave this miniature dollhouse a warm touch. Rita had studied in Heidelberg, and, freshly decorated with her masters degree in philosophy, had accepted a teaching position at the local high school in Heidenheim. Her salary supported us during my remaining years in Darmstadt.

Later in 1952, this room would become our first son's first home. Rita would boil his diapers on that stove and sanitize the baby's bottles on it too. Frau Schutzl allowed us to rinse the cotton diapers in the bathtub of her apartment; otherwise, we could not use it. I built a rack of a sort above the stove to dry the daily wash.

When we brought our little Robert home from the hospital, I read a prayer I had written to greet him.

From my log book, Heidenheim, March 15, 1952:

> *Robert, we bless your coming home into this small room. I, your father, pray at this hour and ask God to grant this blessing. Lord, we, his parents kneel humbly before You and offer to You our lives. In our small way we thank You for this moment. We promise to obey You without fail, as we will share our joy with You and our sorrows. We accept Your justice, Your grace, and Your good will. We ask You to give us courage and strength beyond our own frailty, so we can always choose the best for this innocent child. Please, guide our walk towards Your love. Let us be strong to care, to be hard, just, and forgiving. And now, Robert, I lay you down into this crib I made for you. I tuck you in, and together with God, we start our journey into tomorrow.*

Living in that small room on Horst Heinemann Strasse was not all that easy. We had no space for ourselves. Fortunately, I only lived there during some weekends which made it more bearable for Rita and Rob.

Rob grew into a very sweet little boy, and on his third birthday we moved into a slightly larger apartment. We now had our own bathtub, as our landlord had allowed me to install one in our kitchen. Yes, we had a kitchen, a tiny breakfast niche, and a living room/bedroom arrangement, a palace compared to where we had housed before.

During May of the year, 1954, a letter arrived from America. Rita's girlfriend, Vera, had married an American businessman. They recently had moved to the West Coast. Vera suggested we pull up stakes and bring the family over to live where they were building a house.

Already for quite some time I had decided I would not stay in Germany, the country that had destroyed a good portion of my youth. Too, I felt ashamed of a nation that had gassed and burned people just because they belonged to a different culture and prayed to a God with a different name. I wanted to go to Australia, far away from the blood-soaked European soil.

Quite a few of those why-don't-you-come-over letters came in the mail and, on one Saturday, we talked it over and decided to leave for America.

We told our families.

"Oh my God! You are going to live in that rolled-up-shirtsleeve cowboy land? And to Oregon of all places, so very far away? The grizzlies are running wild there, we hope you know that. Nein, nicht! O mein Got."

Aunts and other well-wishers expressed that New York would have been a better choice.

"Why?"

"Well, it's closer."

I went to the American consulate in Frankfurt and filled out endless reams of application papers. It took over a year to obtain our visa. A problem surfaced right at the start of those lengthy proceedings: I had to pay for the passage before the immigration people would even look at my request. One hundred and eighty dollars per person was quite a chunk of money for us. I had a few Deutschmarks left from my nights as a waiter; friends helped us with the rest.

In Frankfurt, the American doctors took their time to give us a very thorough physical. They, of course, found my heart murmur that had been with me since I had been ill with rheumatic fever; but my wife and son passed without a hitch.

A few weeks later a letter came from Frankfurt saying that they had found some scars inside my colon. That scared me a lot. I returned to Frankfurt where the doctors and I went over my health history one more time. I had forgotten to mention the typhoid fever that I had almost died of in the French camp in Trois Boeuf.

"Mr. Berck, that could be it. We will notify you in about a week."

A month went by. I had almost given up when the complete immigration packet for the three of us arrived. We would be included in the quota sometime next year, after May, 1956.

I still had one more year to finish my diploma. A lot of work had to be done during 1955. I had to furnish finite analysis calculations and the design of two major construction elements for a 700-foot-long bridge spanning the

Rhine. Also, on paper I had to build a short-span, post-stressed box-girder concrete bridge.

The professor in civil engineering had me design a sewer and potable water system for a city of 50,000 people. In mechanical engineering the design of the gearbox for a single-hook, 50-ton harbor bridge crane, turned out to not be a big deal. Did I ever work hard, seven days a week from dawn to midnight! Why should that last year have been any less gruesome than all the other five?

May 15, 1956, the day our journey to America would begin, arrived very fast. The train would leave Heidenheim at six in the morning and bring the three of us to Amsterdam where we were to board the SS Rhinedam, our ship for America.

Late in the afternoon the day before, I had turned in my last written test. I really did not care how it would turn out. No matter what, with or without a diploma, we would go to America. I had been pacing up and down the hallway in front of my master's office. After an eternity the secretary finally had me come in. Dr. Kolb stood behind his heavy oaken desk and took a long look at me.

"Herr Berck!"

He wore his usual white lab coat. A blue tie contrasted against his also white dress shirt. He looked over his thick glasses, pushed way down almost off his nose. Shaking his head ever so slightly, he addressed me again.

"Herr Berck, I let you pass."

My heart took a jump, a big one, a humongous one! Oh my God, I did it!

"I would like you to know your oral performance yesterday did not even come close to my expectations and did not by any means impress me. Forever, please, forever remember that I am doing this only because I know you will leave tomorrow for America."

Who cares? Too happy to feel his insult, I quit listening.

"Here is your diploma. It might come in handy over there. We will mail your formal papers later. Congratulations and good luck."

"Thank you, sir. Dr. Kolb, I have studied here for over six years. I worked very hard for this day, and I want to thank you for those years. I will keep in touch and will let you know how I am faring over there. Good night, sir."

When we shook hands, he did smile at me.

"You have done all right, Mr. Berck."

And for the last time I ran those three kilometers to the railroad station, passing the same destroyed city blocks of homes and houses as I had done for all of those six long years.

It was over!

2

america

My wife Rita, our first son Rob, and I arrived in America on May 24, 1956.

It had been quite the journey. I had no money in my pockets, except for those three Darmstädter emergency dollars. I had held on to them for six years, time enough to bond with each one of them.

I do not remember much of Amsterdam, only the feeling that I had made it. I had in my head an excellent engineering education, and that feeling took precedence over all other events and emotions. No matter how hard I try to remember when we boarded the train, how long it took us to get to Amsterdam, how we managed to find the harbor or the number of suitcases I lugged around, all this does not come to mind.

But when I laid my eyes on the SS Rhinedam, this enormous ocean liner, I halted in awe. She sat at the long dock, heavy sagging ropes tying her to giant iron bollards that stood taller than I. Hundreds of passengers crowded the deck. Yes, I remember that, and the moment when this gigantic vessel slowly pulled away from shore. Everybody waved, many cried. I did neither. Powerful harbor tugs pushed us into the channel.

The large ship drifted toward the ocean, taking me away from hardship and painful memories. I had dared and had succeeded to be free one more time. Nothing would I miss of what I had left behind. An unknown new world already called for new choices, and asked me to set new goals.

That night I wrote in my logbook,

> *there will be new things to discover,*
> *new treasures to be found.*
> *new ways to say yes,*
> *softer to say no.*
>
> *always new will be tomorrow.*
> *so will be yesterday.*
> *new will be the rising sun, and*
> *and so will be the night.*
>
> *new dreams will beg for dawn.*
> *new clouds, tides, and waves,*

new friends I will make.
there always will be a new way
to reach, to share, to tell
of life and peace and love.

I am looking for a word, for an expression that could adequately express my feeling of the unknown power jolting all through me. I felt fulfilled, strong, and very confident that I would make it in the country I had chosen as our new home.

The ocean ahead would be wild—so would be the journey. With every breath I inhaled the dawning of my new future. At this moment I did not care about anything else—nothing.

The ship docked in Southampton, but only for a few hours. That gave us time to move into our stateroom way below on A-deck, where the least expensive cabins housed peasants like us.

Dinnertime! What an experience! People were sitting at long tables decked out with sparkling silverware and fancy napkins, small and large plates, water and wine glasses, and colored dessert bowls. Along the middle of the table sat piles of food, some of which I did not recognize. An army of waiters urged us to try this and taste that. I never ever had seen anything like this. We sat down and I ate until my stomach began to hurt, though the feeling of hunger did not want to go away.

As soon as England faded into the dusk, our ship began to heave with the deep valleys and tall mountains of the ocean's swells. Within a few hours the majority of the passengers were seasick. Breakfast and lunch and dinner for days saw only a few people enjoying them. Rob and I weathered the rolling sea just fine, and we ate and ate. The little boy, just four years old, never left my side. My wife stayed mostly in our cabin, not daring to stray far from her bunk or the small commode.

"Vati, how deep is the ocean?"

Rob held onto me so tightly his little hand turned pale.

"It varies; I'm not sure, Rob. But the teacher in my school told us that somewhere halfway between America and Europe there is a ditch in the bottom of this ocean that is about ten thousand meters deep."

I think Rob could not do much with that information. He kept asking if there were fish that far down, and how the bottom looked, and if one could see down there. I had to assure him many times that our ship would not break in two and sink.

"Vati, say, just in case, would they find us down there?"

Often as far forward as the railing allowed, I stood for hours watching the waves break against the bow of this mighty ship. I could see only sky and mountainous swells and endless horizons, all so majestic! At night the moon would turn the heavy seas into boiling lead, and the rising sun thereafter would change all that into liquid gold.

Still now, whenever I go back to that time and close my eyes, I can feel the waves, I can hear the gusty wind as it tore at my coat.

I am reading from my log book of May, 1956:

> *What a life!*
> *Today is one of those mornings that lets me*
> *feel how immense our world is, how small I am,*
> *and yet how important it is that I walk it tall*
> *and straight. Moments like these are gifts from a*
> *heaven that is so endless, so radiant with light.*
> *Moments like these bear my tomorrow.*

The Statue of Liberty, at the entrance of the harbor, will remain for me an unforgettable moment in time, a moment I can find no words to describe.

Mieschel Morz, the boy in Stukenbrock I had escaped to from the prison camp, had come to America sooner than we. He already had a well-established medical practice on the East Coast in the state of Delaware. His wife, Sheri, a beautiful, charming American young lady, picked us up from Hoboken and showed us around.

"My God, this is America. It is breathtaking!" Those skyscrapers were so very tall!

And then we were standing at Rockefeller Center, where old and young skated on ice seemingly immune to the buzzing environment in this enormous city of New York. On the way to Grand Central Station, Sheri drove us by the bigger-than-life sculpture of a man carrying our whole world on his back. Was it Christopherus? He had carried Christus across the river.

The train rushed us through a strange and vast new country we would call home. So tired were we, the clickity-clacks lulled us into a daze on our not-all-that-comfortable benches. Most of the trip remains a blur, except for the excitement Robert incited when he fell and hit his head on a cast-iron armrest. At the next stop, the big city of Minneapolis, the railroad people brought us to a hospital where Rob got stitched up. To our surprise, they put us up at a hotel and fed us. The next morning an insurance man from the railroad came to call, thrusting in front of us a paper to sign. What it was, I did not know, but now I can guess the document swore we would hold the railroad harmless. For our signatures we were rewarded with a hundred dollar bill. I felt like a king—that C-note would have the company of those three emergency dollars in my pocket.

Our rail journey ended in Portland, a large metropolis at the mouth of the majestic Columbia River in the state of Oregon. It had been a long journey, but one I never repented having undertaken. Similar to the ocean, the prairie, too, had its mighty charm. Day and night the swaying cars had rattled west over tumbleweed country. But in all that beauty inadvertently the death ride from Kreuznach to Rennes in France pushed its ugly scenes into the day. I wondered if that horrible time would ever go away, stay away, and not continuously darken my brightest hours. But time would come when those memories no longer would hurt.

We lived for a month or so with our sponsor, then rented a house, our first home in this great land.

Vera, the friend who had sent all those why-don't-you-come-over letters, helped us find our way into this new society. Her husband, John, my sponsor, went job hunting with me. During the first week in September, 1956, Siebold & Associates, an engineering firm, made me a good offer. Their offices were in a tall building across from the main post office where, after six months, we received our citizenship papers.

A very large lumber construction company retained Siebold to assist with the design of industrial wooden roof structures, both locally and nationwide.

We met with Mr. Bill Smith, the owner of Siebold. He reminded me of Max, Mieschel's father, gentle, his eyes beaming with compassion. I did not quite follow the discussion, because my English still was lousy. Abruptly, or so it seemed to me, Mr. Smith got up, came around his desk, reached for my hand and shook it.

"We'll take you, Paul."

I understood that. I pointed at my diploma on his desk. I wanted him to have a look at it, to understand what I had achieved. That diploma always will be my most important and most precious accomplishment.

"Paul, we go by first names here, I hope you don't mind. I cannot read what's written there. Even if I could, it would not mean much to me. I will watch you for a week or so, and then I will know who you are and how much you can help us."

John and I thanked Mr. Smith and left the office. I was proud at having landed my first job as an engineer, but I was also greatly disappointed! This man had not even glanced at my diploma!

My engineering output surpassed Bill Smith's expectations by a wide margin. The first assignment required me to do a finite analysis on a roof truss that recently had collapsed under a rather light snow load. Why? Well, I went to work using the method of analysis my professor, Dr. Kolb, had chiseled into my brain. It took me about a week. During that time Mr. Smith searched for a professional engineer who could attest to the correctness of my approach. But no one in the area seemed to be familiar enough to judge the validity of my analysis. We finally ended up flying to Madison, Wisconsin, where the dean of structural engineering at the university checked my results. I had never flown before, but soon airplanes would carry me all over the world.

"This is very fine work, Mr. Berck. I happen to be acquainted with your professor, Dr. Kolb, in Darmstadt and also am aware of his curriculum. Presently there are only a few universities in America that teach this type of finite analysis. I'll pass my review on to Mr. Smith. I am glad you came to our country—we need well-educated engineers. It is so good to have met you."

What a relief! I had been right. The truss had collapsed due to an insufficient number of shear washers at one connection.

But the company's engineers still nourished their doubts. I had to design a test truss and predict which member would fail first under overload conditions. I did so and later flew back to witness the test. Luckily the thing came apart at exactly the point my calculations had predicted.

We then went to St. Paul, Minnesota, where Mr. Smith introduced me to the president of Timber West. Of course, I had no clue what it meant to converse with the president of a Fortune 500 company.

Later that afternoon we were sitting in Bill's hotel room when the phone rang.

"Hello, this is Mr. Dave Bernheim's secretary. Mr. Smith, is Mr. Berck with you?"

Bill looked at me. Twisting his face into a question mark, he passed the phone.

"Hello?"

"Hi, this is Dave Bernheim. We met earlier this morning. Would you be so kind as to accept my invitation for dinner tonight?"

Bill, listening, smiled up to his ears.

"Wow, now that is amazing! Do you know... well, let me tell you..."

Shortly thereafter the phone rang again.

"Mr. Berck, there is a limo waiting for you. What shall I tell the driver? Will you be down soon?"

To tell the truth I did not know what the word "limo" meant. Bill straightened my tie and shoved me out the door.

"Be yourself, Paul. I know you can handle that."

The driver, a young man dressed in a slick, snug-fitting chauffeur's uniform, stopped the automobile at the entrance to a giant skyscraper. Looking up, I hardly could see the top floor. A doorman welcomed me. He smiled.

"Guten Abend. Wie geht es Ihnen, mein Herr? Mr. Bernheim is expecting you. This elevator, please. Have a wonderful evening!"

Today I know he expected a good-sized tip, but at that time I only could shake his hand. The elevator sped upwards. Its acceleration reminded me of the coal cage in Shaft #12 in Merlebach.

The door opened and I stepped right into Mr. Bernheim's private dining room. My insecurity kicked in on the double, and I felt remorse for not having accepted his invitation in a much more formal way, though I still do not know how else I could have.

"Hello, hello! May I call you by your first name, Paul? Please, do feel at home here. I am Dave."

He measured a few inches taller than I and wore a light gray, well-fitting suit. We sank into very lush and deep sofa-chairs. Soft indirect lighting and hardly audible music tended to make me whisper rather than talk in a normal tone. Delicate, exotic furniture placed tastefully throughout the spacious room had come from continents far away. The walls and carpet in light maroon calmed my nerves. The actual dining area remained hidden behind a planter hanging above a large saltwater aquarium. Colorful fish between coral and pearl-like air bubbles dreamed of faraway reefs.

"Tell me about yourself, please, and your education. Which university over there is your alma mater?"

I wished someone had made a recording of this conversation. It must have been funny. In my extreme effort to correctly explain myself I sometimes switched to French with him responding immediately in French too. I'm sure he found it amusing, to say the least. In between my broken sentences I sipped my first whisky sour. It tasted awful, and the next chance I had, I bottomed it to get it over with. He smiled.

"Easy. Is this your first acquaintance with hard liquor? Well, if you don't mind, I suggest you drink the next one a little slower."

A few times at home in Heidenheim I'd had too much wine and I remembered the unpleasant consequences.

"Thank you. I should not have another one. It is too strong for me."

Not too many years later I would laugh at those two sentences.

The dinner tasted delicious, I remember that, but what I ate, I do not recall. I became a bit tense while Dave Bernheim talked about his career. An extremely intelligent man articulate and charming, he had traveled the world over and spoke five languages.

He invited me to join him in the living room where steaming coffee was waiting for us in fragile exquisite China porcelain cups.

"Paul, if you like, please tell me some more about your education. I know you must have gone through a rigorous system. The Darmstadt University is known as the number one school in Germany, with an excellent engineering program. Someone told me this morning you have master's degrees in civil and structural and mechanical engineering. What an achievement!"

"It was not easy for me. No money, only little to eat…"

I kept on talking about my life in Darmstadt. He did not interrupt, but once in a while sipped coffee from his cup. I must have rattled on for half an hour or so. Like I said earlier, he probably chuckled all the way through, my English was so rough.

"Paul, if you ever need some help in securing a job up there on the West Coast, here is my card. And now, I believe your plane is leaving very early in the morning. Mr. Smith is probably worried."

Both of us stood up. He came around the low glass table and shook my hand.

"I am glad I met you. Good luck, Paul"

I sneaked by Mr. Smith's door, rid myself of my clothes, and collapsed on my bed. The clock's hand pointed to the two in the morning.

Although I liked my work at Siebold, I needed a second job and found the opportunity at BayShip in Tacoma. The chief engineer there had approached me to do some finite calculations for a crane constructed of non-magnetic steel. The shipyard was building mine sweeper for the US Navy. With Mr. Smith's permission, I worked part-time at the yard. After a few months of racing from one job to the other, BayShip offered me the position of chief mechanical engineer.

In November of 1958, I moved from Siebold to BayShip full-time, with the blessing of Mr. Smith.

This new job had greater challenges in store for me, and my paycheck spelled out larger numbers. Within a year I became the general manager of NorLine, a machinery manufacturing plant with BayShip being the parent company.

During the next few years, Rita gave us three more healthy and beautiful children, Tommy, Martin, and Jessica. After dinner one evening, toward the end of the fifties and the beginning of a new decade, we were sitting on the front porch of our house across the bay from Fox Island. At work I had heard about an aluminum-coated balloon the space agency had shot way high into an orbit around the earth. The evening news reported it, and the *Tacoma News Tribune* predicted that one could see "this thing" with the naked eye.

"… The balloon will appear somewhere south over Anderson Island and then fade into space northerly passing over Seattle…"

Its shiny surface would flex like a sheet of foil. Not a solid sphere, it would tumble and move at a high speed through the night.

Well, maybe so. Things were coming fast, indeed. No one really knew how fast. I looked at my three boys next to me. They were growing up into an uncertain future. The thought of it scared me. I would not have answers for many of their questions. At times I would not even know that they were asking. Someday, although I did not know it yet, I would betray them and not be there to listen to their fears about the future.

I had told the family about the balloon. The sun dipped low behind Fox Island. Dusk lit twinkling lights on the famous suspension bridge that spanned the fast-running Tacoma Narrows.

My wife did not show much interest in space things. Jessica, a baby still, already slept in her crib. But the boys were up, impatiently roaming the house. They could hardly wait, and I, too, expected something un-usual to happen; this "tumbling thing" in the sky, how would it look?

The day took time to lose its light. A cloudless night eventually woke up. The light wind had blown itself to sleep. With blankets, a teddy bear, and pillows, they huddled over their seating arrangement. It never changed. Martin, the youngest would sit between my legs; Rob, son number one, on my left and Tommy, his successor, on my right. But the pecking order needed to be de-cided anew, especially on an evening like this one.

Shortly around ten I shoved Martin off my lap and went to turn off the kitchen lights. Coming back I saw their faces glowing with expectation. Looking at the stars, they were talking about space, the sun, and the moon. Our excitement bubbled out in our words.

To the left, south, we could see McNeil Island with the lights of the federal penitentiary there. To the right, in the distance and way above the incoming tide, the

Narrows Bridge, crawling with tiny cars, coming and going, endlessly, and in slow motion.

I knew the waters of Puget Sound well. My eighteen-foot "Blue Water" boat had a stall at the Steilacoom Marina. I leased an old house at the southern tip of Ketron Island, right by the water and up on a cliff. The family spent most of the summer at this quiet haven—remote, away from the hustling life of the sixties, away from my job, and away from the Top of the Ocean. Built on pilings, this restaurant's bar reached far out to the low-tide level of Commencement Bay. Here I entertained CEOs and military brass with triple-martini lunches, and I stopped there at night on my way home. It was in this place where I began to have a problem with alcohol, though I did not recognize it.

Sometimes I would take my boat from Ketron to my work at NorLine on Commencement Bay. At five in the morning, between tides, the sound lay still, as flat as a sheet of mirror. Clouds floated without a ripple. Scattered layers of thin, gray fog were looking for an out to disappear. The boat scratched a white trail on the dark waters. Left behind, the wake curved with the drift of the sea as I navigated around patches of kelp, driftwood, and floating seaweed.

I zoomed by Steilacoom. A half a mile down, the vast Kaiser Gravel Plant already crushed and conveyed aggregate onto huge stockpiles. A little behind the gravel plant, set back in a cove, the tall smokestack of the *News Tribune's* pulp mill spewed white steam high into the morning air. The loamy cliffs of Fox Island bathed their rich ochre soil in the rising sun. And only a few feet above sea level, almost drowning, Day Island ahead had yet to wake up.

The outgoing tides rush through the Narrows at fifteen, sometimes twenty knots, pulling my boat fast along the shoreline. But as soon as I swung easterly, the colliding waters at Point Defiance bucked me. I needed to slow down anyway. Dozens of small fishing boats bobbed up and down trying to avoid the whirlpools of the fighting currents. Fishing rods arched like they were conducting an orchestra with idling motors and lapping ripples that splashed against the skiffs. I always made a wide sweep. To the east and now right in front of me, Mount Tahoma poked its icy peak into a golden-blue sky.

The boat bounced hard through the wake of the Vashon ferry. Picking up speed again, I whisked by the Tacoma Smelter, Harbor Lights, and the Top of the Ocean, my watering holes, all still recovering from the night before.

Rob's elbow nearly pierced my left thigh as he pointed to the bridge.

"Vati, is it really true that a few years back this big bridge fell down? My teacher says the pieces are still lying at the bottom of the Narrows, yes?"

"Yeah, the wind took it, made it bounce until the structure finally snapped. A professor from the University of Washington happened to be right there, filming this grossly swaying 'Galloping Gertie' when it swung itself out of existence. Rob, you saw that film more than once. Remember tourists watching the movie through the large show window of the bridge's tollhouse? I saw it in Germany, during my days in Darmstadt."

I must have told them this story a hundred times, yet their eyes still hung on every word I said. Such rapt attention always served to remind me how much I loved our children.

"Vati, are those the holes in the roadway Martie calls 'windows to the water'?"

Whenever we drove over the bridge to go to the Kalaloch beach on the Pacific Ocean, Martin would let them all know.

"Vati, I can see the water. There are windows in the bridge. Look, Tommy, look."

And after an hour or so had gone by, Martie would ask if our car ever could fall through one of those "windows."

"No, no! But some people are afraid of just that. It makes them drive slower, and the traffic often slows down to almost a halt."

"When is this thing coming?"

No one answered. Fidgety, pushing, tucking blankets, and wiggling on their little rumps with their eyes wide open, they waited impatiently. Silence usually lived in our house only during the deep of the night—unless we had sore throats or bad dreams.

All of a sudden little Martin broke into that hushed moment.

"Vati, what does... no... what is 'eterity'?"

"It's not 'eterity,' stupid. 'E-T-E-R-N-I-T-Y.' Get it? Did you sleep through catechism class?"

Rob, the oldest tried to get away with being a smart guy. Little Martin didn't go to school yet. He didn't know about catechism.

"I'm not stupid. Vati, you tell him. Okay, Rob, you're so smart, you tell me what 'eterity' is, or whatever you call it."

Rob crossed his legs yoga fashion, twitched around a little, and looked at Martin. Just as he opened his mouth to say something, Tommy broke in, no longer able to hold back.

"Eternity, Martie, is where they have no watches, and nobody tells time anymore. The clocks no longer tick. I think, it's daytime there all the time." He was a year and a half older than Martin, one could tell. And as so often, Rob ignored Tommy's explanation.

"L o o k—the thing, the balloon! Look, Vati, look! It's so shiny! See, geeee! Oh, look, look!"

Martie, shaking all over, wrapped my arms tightly around him.

We could see the balloon coming, speeding high above, racing through the black sky. We followed its path as the silvery sphere tumbled high in the sky. It appeared far mightier than I had expected.

The wonder of the moment took the words from our mouths. The balloon slithered through the night, traveling very fast as it disappeared on its way to Seattle. Then, the boys busted the silence, whooping and exploding with their questions all at the same time.

Space, what is space? Where is it, how big? This balloon made of silsver? Will it come back? Where will it land? What are stars made of? Where is the sun now? Sleeping? God lives in space, yes? The man in the moon, he has a house and a dog like we have? What is bigger, heaven or space? Is heaven in the sky or what? God lives in heaven, not in space?

"Where is the balloon now?"

"Must have been windy, it went so fast. How high…?"

Little Martin rubbed the back of his head into my stomach.

"Couple of miles or so," Tommy volunteered.

Rob raised his eyebrows, gave me his knowing look, meaning, "God, they really don't know from up!"

"More than two miles, turkey, much more."

Tommy, ever so slightly tilted his head, looked up to me, his eyes defiant: Ha, they said, Rob doesn't know for sure either.

Martie shoved into Rob.

"Hey, you guys, like always, nobody answers my questions. D o   y o u   h e a r ?   Vati, come on, tell me about this 'eterity,' pleeeeeeeze."

Martin complained always that no one ever listened to him. But listening to him meant listening right now, this very moment, immediately and completely! Sometimes tears ran down his angel face, his piercing eyes demanding instant attention and all that goes with that. Years have come and gone, and to this day nothing has changed. If anything, his demands for our acknowledgement come more urgently than ever.

"Okay, OKAY!"

How could I explain eternity? I had tried some time ago to do that when Ludwig's friends sat on my bed at the Holzmann house in Ansbach.

What is eternity? What does it mean? Though I had been pondering that for years, I still had not heard an answer I could understand. But the children wanted to know.

"I will try. I am not so sure what eternity is or what it means. Imagine eternity is a day without a dawn, a day without a sunset, like this evening without tomorrow morning. Tommy is pretty close, I think. Eternity could be a time, a place where the clock keeps ticking, but the hands of it no longer move.

"I do not know, but eternity may not be only in the future. It always has been and will be going on forever. Your mother says it has to do with God. Of course, everything has to do with God, sooner or later."

Rob looked puzzled.

"Vats, you say, we are living in eternity now? I mean right now, this moment? I don't, geez, I don't get it, Tommy's deal with the clock not ticking. No, I'm confused."

Tommy had fallen asleep. Little Martin earlier had crashed on the floor next to the coffee table in the living room. A light breeze rasped the hard leaves of the madrona tree in the corner by the fence. The taste of rotting kelp, which the last tide had brought ashore and left there to die, wallowed up from the beach and scented the night.

"Vati, can we go with the boat off Fox Island and snorkel for geoducks this weekend?"

I gave Rob a hug.

"I will have to be in Boston this coming week. Come, help me with Martie here."

I cradled up Tommy and tucked them in. Their souls are my eternity. Could that be it?

Rita was in bed, reading. I sat next to her. A hug, I needed a hug.

"I listened to you explaining eternity to the children. You just don't get it, do you now?"

"What?"

Still, no hug.

I went and took a shower. Through the swishing of hot water prickling my tired body, I heard her filtered voice. "… God… just… God."

I came back into a dark bedroom.

Good night? I bedded down and pulled the blanket way over my head. Turned away, I longed for someone who would go with me. Someone I could share my doubts with, the war, the horrible years in the prison camp, the years I had dared death so many times. I needed someone who would listen to what I could not talk about.

Closing my eyes not to see the dark, I thought of Kate.

Kate, I know you would cradle my soul. I know you would listen and understand. You were there when God used words we did not know what to do with, when it seemed He did not want to answer at all.

I miss you, Kate. After so many years I still hear your voice. Those short moments with you in Mannheim, after my escape, will not fade. And I don't want them to. I keep them in my heart. I should have stayed with you then, yes, I should have.

At the office the next day we all talked about the balloon. Space, Sputnik, and Kennedy committing the nation to walk on the moon within the decade occupied our minds.

Friday night a United Airlines red-eye special flew me to Chicago and on to Boston. During the sixties the airplane had become my second home. I usually arrived at the airport only ten minutes before departure time. My tickets were always waiting for me in the airline's VIP room. Mr. Keck, United Airlines' CEO, had presented me with a 100,000-miler plaque.

I knew most of the first class stewardesses by name. A drink, a pillow, a blanket, and everything else. I never needed to ask.

After a late snack, I drank the rest of my Bordeaux, the deep red wine born along the shores of the River Garonne.

A year ago, NorLine had come out with an improved design of our large tuna seine winch. The skipper of the Spanish vessel who had purchased one invited me to be on board during sea trials and to assist with the testing and training of his crew. On my way to San Sebastian at the Spanish-French border, I stopped at the city of Bordeaux and visited its beautiful twelfth-century Romanesque Basilica of Sainte Croix. The floor inside the church is done in large slabs of gray sandstone. Coming up the granite stairs to the portal, the slates, worn by seven hundred years of worshipping, still showed names and dates. Cardinals, prelates, and priests were laid to rest beneath those stones. I could read a faint 1202 on a slab to the left of the main entrance.

Actor Dustin Hoffman, one day in the future seventies, would be marching through the crooked narrow streets of lower Bordeaux, and by this church, as he played his role in the film *Papillon*.

Knita, the stewardess, brought me a warmed glass of Courvoisier, an exquisite French cognac, and sat down beside me. The lights in the airplane had been all but turned off.

Through the low hum of the jet's turbine I heard her ask, "Where are you going to this time? DC again?"

"No, to Boston."

"I'm dead-heading in Boston the day after tomorrow. I'll be home for a couple of days."

Her hair touched my face. She reached, searching for my hand, took it, and leaned her head into it.

Why did I like that moment? Was it because it took away the pressures of my job, or was it something I could not find at home? Did it have to do with me shrugging off responsibilities I had promised to take on and to execute? Or did the jerk in me float to the surface?

Ever since the balloon night, I had begun to veer off the path I had promised to walk no matter what. My drinking became more than just a social act. One drink or two no longer were enough. I needed four, even five, before I would start to feel comfortable with myself and the world around me. For unknown reasons I began to feel lonesome. I felt not needed other than for bringing home an ever-increasing paycheck. I became a stranger in my house. Many a night I came home reeking with guilt and booze. My wife knew of my infidelities. The children often saw me coming home drunk, until I no longer came home before they went to bed. I would open the door to their room and for a minute stand there watching them sleep. I did and I do love my children. What made me betray them, I do not know.

Oh yes, I argued with my conscience and asked why I ran away from my family, looking elsewhere for companionship, compassion, and acknowledgement. What drove me away from the safe haven of my home, and from the real values I once had cherished? Alcohol tranquilized my guilt. Sick with power and money, I no longer looked in the right places to find what I was missing. Why? Love. I wanted to be loved, I wanted to be loved. I wanted to be accepted as a partner. Rita once told me that I did not know what love is, and probably I didn't. Maybe I had not been taught what love is all about. Maybe that's why I did not find it at home. During the earlier years I equated love with giving all, not needing an echo coming back filling my soul. I thought I had to make others happy at any price and that would buy me love.

The outside world seemed to understand me, the overworked executive, the super-salesman, the most charming guy to be out with, the manager who cared for his people. Mr. Arnsen, the owner of BayShip, said it many times, "What you touch, Paul, turns into money. You're a good man."

A passenger a few rows behind us pushed the service button and Knita went to see how she could help. She did not come back right away, and I rehearsed my speech for the next day. Scientists at Woods Hole near Martha's Vineyard had invited me to give a presentation and familiarize them with our newly developed constant tension feature. It allowed for launching and retrieving deep-sea research equipment and mini-submarines at heavy sea stages. But I could not concentrate. I kept thinking about Rob's disappointed face when I had hugged him good-bye.

I got pen and paper and wrote a letter to him.

"Rob. Hi. I'm up here at 38,000 feet. A while back the captain walked by and told me that the outside thermometer reads -95 degrees F. I know him from a recent flight to New Orleans, when he invited me to fly with him, sitting in the cockpit's jump seat of his brand new 707 Boeing jet. This one-time privilege came with that 100,000-mile award I told you about, which is hanging in my office.

Just after takeoff, the moon came out over Mt. Rainier. Lots of snow still up there. I saw a cloud hovering near the peak. It had an odd shape, like a fat pancake. Through my pinched eyes it looked like a spacecraft. Very strange and eerie!

"What if? Would those aliens have better answers for us?

"You know, I always get excited thinking about time. What is time? Who made it? Who made the very first nano-second tick? Are we people here on this planet, in our solar system, in our Milky Way galaxy, the only ones, the only ones who know time? Exploding stars yonder, spinning billions of light years in the distance, do they have the same hours of the day as we have?

"On that 'balloon night' a few days ago, we talked about eternity and infinity. Do these words mean the same? Is eternity the religious name for infinity? Neither one is supposed to have a beginning nor an end. It puzzles me too. It is mind-boggling at best. The moment a second is born, in this same instant it is dead already. And who is counting time? God? Your mother thinks so."

Knita's voice came over the intercom.

"… Please, put your tray tables up and return the backs of your seats to the upright position.…"

Chicago, we were coming in over the northwestern shoreline. The city below began to wake up. I liked landing in Chicago. For me it seemed more exciting than touching down in LA or New York. I still have an oil painting I did during the mid-sixties. Trying to arrest the view of this nightly city, I covered quite some canvas; Chicago, with the moon on the dark waters of the lake. Majestic! Beautiful!

I buckled up.

"Well, I didn't say much to answer little Martin's question about eternity. I did not even come close to what I wanted to share with you. Rob, I feel so small, so lost when I think about time and its consequences. Could it be that it only exists because we are watching it? Love you, Vati."

On the way out, Knita hugged me with a penetrating, tempting smile on her face.

"See you soon, Paul. Try to be good."

Her parents were from Russia, St. Petersburg. I had met her the first time in San Francisco, waiting for a cab.

"Hi. I'm Paul. Want to share the ride? Holiday Inn at the Fisherman's Wharf?"

"Yes, thank you. I stay at a place near the Coit Tower. The driver can drop me off there first. My name is Knita."

During the flight from Chicago to Boston's Logan Airport I took a nap. After I landed, a cab brought me to the Hilton. I entered the stuffy room. That certain hotel-smell that sleeps between sheets, blankets, and bath towels instantly stuck to me. Hot, hot shower, quick shave, clean shirt, clean teeth, and I came to.

The drive to Woods Hole turned out to be pleasant. Some small towns along the way were still sleeping. Rolled up newspapers in plastic bags littered many driveways.

My presentation at 11AM began on time.

"Good morning, ladies and gentlemen! Thank you for inviting me. Allow me to start my presentation by sharing an incident that happened to me; no, not on the way to this studio, but on my way home from my last trip to Boston.

"My friend, Vince, has a maple tree orchard some-where near here. His hobby is zapping his trees to make their juice run into small cups tied to the trunks. Magically, after a while, this stuff turns into pure golden maple syrup. I had stayed at his place with his wonderful, loving family of nine children. The morning we parted, he bestowed upon me a pint of this elixir vita.

"Embedded between my dirty laundry, the container, a metal can, saw itself unable to withstand the negative pressure at 42,000 feet up in the sky. Relieving itself, it sweetened my personal effects, sharing its ambience. In the restroom at SeaTac, my leather fold-up began to show stickiness near the fold. I do not know what or who made me do this, but I left the bag there and hurried away.

"A few days later my secretary received a phone call. The bag would be delivered shortly at my office. My tag had given away my number. The folks at our plant still do not want to forget this 'sweet' incident."

Like any other speaker would, I let the applause simmer a bit while I sipped ice water from the glass by the lectern.

"And now, please return to the main menu. The constant tension tapered cable storage drums of our NorLine deep sea coring winch are controlled by tension sensors mounted on the fairlead…"

I patted myself on the back. What a terrific speaker I was. I had their attention.

The next day I assisted the procurement engineer in charge with writing the specifications in such a way that made it nearly impossible for other winch builders to furnish a bid. It had been done many times to us at NorLine. I invited the purchasing agent and his wife for dinner. We met at a "members only" restaurant on the waterfront north of Woods Hole and dined on delicately smoked oysters and soft-shell crab. I remember faintly the price of the bottle of Chianti to have been around $85— a small fortune at the time.

During the sixties nobody raised an eyebrow regarding this open practice to entertain government officials and CEOs of large and influential companies. It had taken me a while to catch on, but I caught up in a hurry. Frequently I would provide after-hours entertainment. Competitors and big suppliers occasionally would pass out a credit card to a purchasing agent with a $50,000 spending limit, no questions asked. No, I am not making this up. Those were accepted standards of doing business at the time. I personally refused to take advantage of this type of gratitude, but I was a generous donor.

Back in Boston I learned Knita had changed my original departure date and time. Both of us lived through a careless day, went to a movie, and strolled along the waterfront. All very beautiful, but it had nothing to do with love. It left me lonely, so very lonely. Still, I did not dwell on it. The next drink would ease the situation.

I flew back to Seattle Sunday evening. I did not go home, but prepared the work order for the new winch Woods Hole had bought. Their purchase order carried a footnote, saying that, due to a rather short delivery cycle and the special nature of the equipment, the usual bidding procedures had been suspended. Wonderful!

Around three in the morning I went to sleep in a comfortable reclining chair in my office. At six I showered in the shop's locker room and changed clothes. Trisha, my administrative assistant, brought fresh coffee, and both of us sat there for a while, smoking our cigarettes.

She saw to it that I had at least one complete set of clean and ironed clothes in my office closet. So often it happened that I had to take the next available plane to Washington, DC, or Pascagoula, where I attended procurement conferences at Ingals Shipyards.

This soft chair of mine also became important on Friday afternoons. On that day Mr. Arnsen would stop by my office. Stretched out on my chair, he would light up his cigar and get down to business.

"Paul, you're not making any money. You are losing our shirt here...."

Before he came over from the shipyard, Francesca, his confidante and secretary, always armed him with a torn-off piece of adding machine tape showing the three most important figures in any business: work in progress, accounts receivable, and accounts payable.

Needless to say, these numbers often were not congruent with the ones my accountant had come up with. So we argued a little, but only for the sake of it. He firmly believed we were underperforming. Nothing in my power would change that opinion of his. I knew we were doing better than just all right.

By four o'clock or so, he would ask me to have a drink with him. I would go to the beautiful wood liquor cabinet, custom made for me by Oscar, the yard's top cabinet maker, and fix the drinks. Trisha had taken care of the ice cubes in the bucket. He liked expensive Scotch and smooth Canadian whiskey.

We'd have a few drinks, chat, and gossip some 'til around six when he drove his Cadillac home.

By the end of the sixties, life handed me a terrible blow. Rob overdosed during his desperate search for a life away from our collapsing family. That made me stop drinking for a few days and, partially sober, it became clear to me that I had to change my life. I needed to start walking in a different direction if I wanted to survive my alcoholism and get well. My reflection in the mirror no longer looked like me. I did not like myself anymore. I realized I had failed and needed to start over again.

I tried to convince Rita to go with me to Canada where I would stake out a homestead near Milepost 500. I thought I could shake all this in the pristine nature somewhere in the Yukon Territory. But my wife did not want to go with me. "Pioneering," as she put it, meant living without a culture. I did not then and I do not now hold that against her. Could she have trusted me?

We divorced by the end of the sixties.

I rented a small U-Haul trailer, and loaded it up with the few belongings I was allowed to call mine. My VW pulled it north over the Alcan Highway to Alaska.

Looking over my whole life, to leave the children was and still is the most painful moment I can remember. It hurt at least as much as the hour when I stood at Tommy's grave some years later. But if I would not have left, I possibly would have destroyed their lives even more. I wanted to get well at any price.

To find a job in Anchorage turned out to be quite a task. The start of the crude oil pipeline construction had been delayed by the federal government's requirement for an environmental impact statement. My résumé showing I had been a vice president in the lower forty-eights closed many doors. At that time, Anchorage attracted many people from all over the USA who had failed at their jobs at one time or another. Those who had found a job felt threatened by guys like me. Rejects were scared of rejects.

"We are truly sorry, but the job you have applied for does not require such an overqualified person as you are," became a familiar refrain.

Eventually I did find a good and rewarding position with the Greater Anchorage Borough. I became their first central procurement officer.

In time I found a new partner. We lived a peaceful life. Forever do I need to thank Tanya for loving me and for getting me off the bottle. We bought an airplane, a Cessna 150, "6732 Golf," and I learned to fly. I liked it up there so close to heaven. We went shopping for groceries in that plane; or, on the spur of the moment, we would fly to Kenai Lake and have dinner there.

One summer night we flew to Talkeetna. The flight had been majestic. Before we landed on that rather short, gravel strip with high trees at either end, we had cruised along side Mount McKinley. The sun bathed the blue snow and ice crevices in magic light. We left the restaurant after dinner in broad daylight, walking along the wooded path that led to the runway.

I had tethered plane at the other end of the strip. As we approached, we suddenly halted and froze. A tall brown bear played with the plane's tie-down ropes like they were strings on an oversized cello. We watched for some time. I became concerned he would rip the cab door open and clean out the cockpit, so we went back to the restaurant where the owner, much to our surprise, began to laugh.

"Yeah, he does that once in a while, but he'll do no harm. Come, I'll go with you."

We followed him; but when the three of us looked, we did not see any bear anywhere.

"You're sure? I mean, did you really…?"

I made the man go with us and had him stand there until I revved up the engine, grinning at him as I took to the gravel. I loved that airplane, and I did a lot of stupid stunts with it, like flying at 3,000 feet in a 50-knot, 45-degree crosswind, or clipping tree tops when landing on very short strips. Dumb things, yes, but I had my fun. Flying over the Hardy ice fields, or cruising above the Matanuska Glacier, was exhilarating. I remember one night Tommy and I flew up the Susitna River, cruising at not more than ten feet above the water. Those moments I keep. They are too beautiful to ever let go.

Tanya, my friend, a very gifted artist, carved sculptures from soapstone, birch, and cottonwood bark. She taught me to make cups and vases from Anchorage's Bootleggers Cove clay. I learned from her what colors to use and how much of it to put on. We fired our pottery in straw fires or in natural gas ovens. Her art spoke of deep feelings and understanding of the mighty nature around.

In 1971 Rob, well again, came to Anchorage; so did Tommy and Martin. Tanya, my wife by then, was a good mother to them, very kind and outgoing, freely wanting to help and to give. The boys went to high school up on the hill by Huffman Road, although Tommy soon decided to go back to Seattle. Martin became the Alaska state champion in wrestling before he graduated. For a while, Rob worked in Anchorage, but then left to go to college somewhere south. Jessie and her mother went back to Germany, where Jessie graduated from high school. She returned later to Seattle and studied at the university for her masters degree in economics.

In 1980, I began to drink again. It happened far away from our western world, and on the opposite half of our planet.

3

far east

I walked into a new world vastly contrasting the one I had left only hours ago. Taiwan, an island floating in the South China Sea, engulfed me. Hot, humid air tinted with a peculiar fragrance soaked my shirt. Chinese hieroglyphics everywhere cryptically kept their meaning from me.

Arriving past midnight, bushed and beat, I dragged my stuff through complex immigration procedures. Fifteen hours on the plane and the long layover in Tokyo had sapped me. And night and day were now twisted around. Luckily, my visa and all required fees seemed to be okay.

"Miestaw Birck, patrol boats? Where? You ben in mainland China befoa? You health? Enough money foa stay heea?"

"I never have been in mainland China. The boats are moored at China Shipyard in Kaohsiung. I am healthy, all is okay."

Satisfied, the man in green stamped my passport. He bowed several times, smiling profusely, wishing me, "Goot trip, goot trip!"

A new thing for me—everybody in Taiwan bowed. I liked these humble interchanges, and ever since then I have combined my handshake with a slight bow.

The Sungshan airport turned out to be not a user-friendly place. Outside, some twenty cab drivers surrounded me. All wanted to take me to the hotel. They started to fight over my bags. I finally turned to one and shoehorned myself into his small cab.

The Grand Hotel, an impressive place up on the hill, north of the city, held my reservation. The guest pamphlet claimed the hotel's new roof to be the largest classical Chinese roof on earth. It appeared to be immense! It took the cab over half an hour to get there. I paid the driver with a $10 bill. The next day I would get new Taiwan dollars, called "NTs," and find out that those ten bucks could have gotten me halfway to Kaohsiung. The bellboy also let me know that my cabdriver had taken the longest way possible to get to the hotel, and that I had contributed generously to the economy.

In the morning a cab brought me to the domestic airport of TaiBei, as they called it there.

Checking my bags, I listened to the music coming from hidden speakers throughout the airport. First I thought it could not be, but then... yes, the "Raindrop Prelude." Chopin in Taiwan? Père Lachaise, the famous cemetery in Paris, came to my mind, and Chopin's white marble sarcophagus under a sea of flowers the visitors left there every day.

The plane took me to Kaohsiung, the island's southern seaport. Sitting in seat A1, I had a clear view of the Chungyang Range, a ragged mountain crest, reaching some three thousand feet into the sky. It stretched along the eastern part of the island down to the very southern tip.

M̲r. Huff, the president of BayShip in Tacoma, had called me in Anchorage and had asked me to come back and join the team.

"We have a very special task waiting for you."

Ten years had gone by since I had left there, and I hesitated to start over again. But Mr. Huff informed me the company had changed hands, and that he happened to be the new owner and CEO.

On May 17, 1980—I remember that day—I talked it over with Tanya. She did not encourage me.

"Paul, we live a good life here. You run the operations of the largest gravel mining and aggregate company in Alaska. The money they pay you is close to six figures. We can buy a bigger airplane, if you want that. And then the engineering work you have done here has been acknowledged nationwide. People around here know you and admire you. Why would you leave all this? We have enough money. We can retire right now."

All that was true. Why, then, did I want to leave Anchorage, go back, take on new responsibilities, and face new uncertainties? Yes, I could have retired, but I did not feel old enough to do that. And to be honest, I did not want to be "taken care of." At fifty-three I still wanted to go places, take on challenges, do new things, prove the old dog still had teeth. I had enough candle left to burn for a long time. No, this "we should take it easy" did not ring true with me. There also was another reason why I felt I needed a change. I saw my love for Tanya withering away. I had no explanation for this. It just happened. Those were the days when I began to realize that I was no good at keeping relationships with women I had promised to stay with—a flaw in my character.

No, ten years in Alaska were enough, and by the end of May, 1980, I accepted the position of vice president at BayShip. This decision, though, invited disastrous consequences. It would coax me back into the same cage from which I thought I had escaped—the alcohol. The way it happened, no one could have guessed.

BayShip had built gunboats for the Taiwanese Navy. During recent maneuvers the propulsion gearboxes overheated. For nearly a full year, efforts to correct this embarrassing situation had failed. Evidently, I would be inheriting a rundown engineering department.

During my first staff meeting, Mr. Huff assured me, "Paul, we know you can fix that problem and reestablish our credibility."

I studied the drawings and felt confident he had not misplaced his trust.

I picked up my bags from the baggage carousel and met Ken, BayShip's superintendent and liaison between Tacoma and Kaohsiung. He had been living in that city for quite some time.

The thermometer topped a hundred that afternoon. Wet air mixed with my sweat darkened my blue shirt. Our cab literally crawled ahead, drowned in thousands of motor scooters and bicycles. It seemed as though the whole city moved during shift change. Over two million people lived in this second largest city of Taiwan.

I watched with fascination. Some riders wore safety helmets, but most pedaled and scootered under their familiar coned straw hats. Amazing! A man driving a Taiwanese Vespa had three kids standing between his arms in front of him. His woman, in lady-fashion on the back seat, held on to a couple of plastic grocery bags while her baby slept in a pouch slung over her shoulder.

"Ken, look at that guy with the oxygen bottle strapped to the basket on his bicycle. Man, are they crazy? See, the safety cap is missing!"

Frightening memories surfaced. Merlebach, at the welding shop back in 1947 in the French prison camp...

François unloaded full oxygen bottles from his truck. He unscrewed the safety cap to get a better grip when he let the bottle slide down from the truck bed. I took it and rolled it upright to the nearby rack and reinstalled the cap. It had been a routine operation. One Friday afternoon François got careless. He had had too many at lunch. A bottle slipped through his hands and hit the concrete floor. It fell flat on its side. Jumping to safety, I saw the valve breaking off as it hit the running board of his truck. The bottle turned into a rocket. Pressurized by three thousand pounds per square inch of oxygen, it took off with an awesome hiss and drilled itself through the cement block wall of our shop. It had missed Monsieur LaTone, but not by much. The bottle came to rest at the foundation supporting a huge cement silo that afterwards leaned like the Tower of Pisa.

"You will get used to it. Trust me, Paul. That is the way things are around here. Wait till you see people on their bicycles transporting live chickens in boxes stacked five high."

Sticky all over, I checked in at the Kingdom Hotel on WUFU #4 Road. The manager bid his welcome and ushered me to room 422.

"You, please, ring bell when you need. Floor manager will come. We like Ken, your company, very good customer. Have goot stay. Do you need woman?"

"What do you mean?"

"O, Miestaw Paul, you new heea. Ken know, he tell you."

We exchanged our see-you-laetaw bowings until he, walking backwards, disappeared in the elevator. Like in England, one does not show one's back ever to the Queen.

The cool air-conditioned room, the very long shower, and the fresh clothes made me whole again. I even remembered to keep my mouth closed during the shower. My doctor at home had suggested that as a preventive measure to stem off typhoid-related symptoms.

I found Ken in the bar on the second floor downstairs.

"Hey, Tony, this is the man I told you about."

"Hello, Tony. I am Paul Berck."

"Good, nice to see you here. You need anything, let me know. Ken says you can fix the problem. I understand it will take a good man to do that. How about a Dr Pepper?"

Surprisingly he spoke good English. Something else I would have to get used to: Nobody kept anything to himself. Everybody knew what he and she and they were up to. So naturally Tony already knew about me and my preferred soft drink. I laughed.

"Tony, how do you know it's Dr Pepper?"

"Well, we know things. But believe you me, you'll get sick around here without alcohol. Don't ever drink our water."

"Ken, you are one hell of an advance man. How'd you know about it?"

"Chester, the manufacturing VP. You are hooked on that stuff, right? Come and meet some of the other reps."

"Joe, this is Paul, the big wheel from the BayShip's engineering department. Joe here is the turbine man from GE, and Buster next to him is a Raytheon rep from the radar outfit in Lexington, Massachusetts. They oversee the installation of their stuff at China Shipyard."

"Hey, guys. Good to meet you all!"

With two Dr Peppers down, I left with Ken to get some dinner.

"Okay, show me the town."

I would work well with Ken. I had not met him before, but I felt comfortable with him right away. We cabbed from bar to bar or better, from club to club. Dr Pepper began to run out of my ears.

"Do you like any of those girls?'

"What do you mean? Sure. Different, yes, but very beautiful."

I had not just gotten off the bus. I knew what Ken meant, but was not quite sure I wanted to share that kind of confidence yet.

Moulin Rouge, Pigalle, Paris, what a trip. Quite the show.

"Hey, Paul, come on, it's okay. Hsiu is my friend. She works at the Westminster Club not far from here."

The cab slid into a hard left. We got out and Ken paid the driver.

Club Westminster, what a friendly place! Incense hazed the air. Hushed laughter mingled with the clicking of glasses. Red, gold-trimmed lanterns gave just enough light to enhance an already laid-back atmosphere. A short bar on either side of the room framed a few soft chairs and low tables in the center of a not too spacious layout. Some men sat on comfortable high stools at the bar. The maidens were busy with fixing drinks, offering teasing entertainment. In the background, so very smoothly and sentimentally, Elvis Presley did his "Heartbreak Hotel." It sure didn't fit, but neither did it interfere with the mood.

Joe and Buster were playing cards with a couple of girls. We sat down, and I began to relax. Leaning back in my chair, I mused about all these new and strange things that were coming at me.

Ken introduced Hsiu. Very pretty. Ken had good taste, no question about that.

"Gaân kuâi, Toi. Come meet Miestaw Paawl." She waved for her friend behind the bar, made her sit next to me, and then hopped onto Ken's lap. He leaned over.

"Toi. Listening to the others I think it's close to 'Toyjee.' But she might teach you better how to say her name."

She stood taller than the other women in the place, taller than most on this island. She knew of some English words.

"I, Toi. Hi. Ken here say, you good man. I bring Dr Pepper. Okay?"

Again, that Dr Pepper, Ken had prepared them for my arrival. Everyone seemed to follow a script. But I didn't want any more pop.

"A beer is fine. One isn't going to hurt. Right, Ken?"

Why I said that, did that, is still beyond me. I knew it would take only one beer, one drink, and it would be all over. I had not touched a drop, nor had I had a smoke in seven years.

As if on cue, Toi said, "I have cigarette. Here."

"Okay, Ken, all bets are off. Hmm, I can always say you led me astray."

"Excuse me, sir. I was told that could not be done. Relax, this isn't a bad life. These are good people. Get to know them, Paul."

We left Westminster. Hsiu and Toi took us dancing at another club close by. On the seventh floor, the elevator opened into a throbbing disco crowd. We could not find a table. But Ken knew how to get one. He had been there before. I danced with Toi to sweet music and slow old songs.

"... put your head upon my pillow..." With her arms folded around me, she let me feel her body.

"You shy man?"

I did not answer, but held her tighter and stroked her hair. What, what am I doing? Did I drink already too much of this strong Taiwan beer? I only have had two.

Hsiu wanted to do the next tango with me. I looked to Ken for his okay.

"Ken, I can tango with Hsui?"

"If I said no, would that go on my report card? Sure it's okay. I begin to see it will take me a while to figure you out."

"Tell me when you're done. I always wanted to know." I knew the scouting report Ken had gotten on me probably said "happily married, doesn't drink, not a swinger." His confusion as he watched me dance intimately with these exotic women told me he was quickly revising his opinion.

I swayed Hsiu through "... my cup runneth over..." She looked up at me.

"Toi like you. You good man. She sweet girl. She my friend, you good to her."

"We are going to take a walk, Ken."

"Do you know what time it is?"

"You care?"

We walked up the hill to the Shoushan Park. The city, dotted with haloed lights, spread out below us, warm and humid. The stars in the sky blinked differently from those at home, a continent afar.

"Toi, these stars are..."

"Paul, you not happy, no?"

"I am okay, Toi. Your country, your city, and you— all is so new to me. I really don't know what to say or do. I am a little lost sitting here next to you."

But inside me I felt a variant, vibrant life somewhere waiting for me. A life, bearing changes and challenges, uncertainty and even pain.

She put her arm around my waist.

"I like you, Paul. You not like other men. You not lie to me."

Searching for my hand, she found it shaking. We had just spoken a few words, traded shy glances. A few hours only had passed. Yet every moment had been flooded with uprooting, deep feelings I sensed would bring a new tomorrow. And I wanted a new tomorrow. Where did all this unrest in me come from? So help me, I still do not know.

Sunday, yet I asked Ken to go to the shipyard with me. I wanted to get a feel for the situation. The bellhop whistled for a taxi. We wore thin, short-sleeved cotton coveralls that instantly clung to our backs as we stepped outside.

The cab dropped us off at the security building at the shipyard. Ken waved his pass. Still, it took a long time to get a one-day permit for me. We boarded the yard bus for the repair shop building.

"Ken this looks like any other day in the week. Do they work seven days?"

"Yes, they do. The whole city works seven days a week—stores, doctors, you name it."

China Shipyard, the most modern shipbuilding facilities in the Far East, spreads over hundreds of acres. Two immense graving docks, inverted dry docks, accommodated super tanker building programs that produced one vessel per month.

Ken had called ahead for Mr. Chen, the shop foreman, to meet us at the shop.

"Hello, Mr. Chen. This is Paul Berck from BayShip, the gearbox-man I told you about who will fix things."

"Ah, ah, Miestaw Paawl, we hope, we hope." I bowed.

"Good morning, Mr. Chen. Thank you for coming this morning. I hope we did not disturb your Sunday. But I am anxious to start testing tomorrow."

"Hohkey, hohkey Miestaw Paawl, hohkey. Not problem."

We discussed the plan of attack. Mr. Chen would have things ready on Monday morning. A small crew of mechanics would be on hand.

"Ah, Monday, hohkey, hohkey, tsank a you, tsank a you."

Politely bowing we stepped back into the bus and left the yard.

Ken went on to Westminster. I checked for messages at the hotel and went up to the bar on the second floor. A cold beer, yes! Toi, already there, motioned for me to come and sit by her. Tony filled an iced beer glass with the foam sliding down the jug.

"Hey, man, how is your day? Here. It's on the house."

"Good to see you. I missed you, girl."

I gave Tony my report, and with that contributed to the agenda of this very communicative society.

"We go your room. You take shower, and then we eat at nice fish place. You like fish?"

"In this heat?"

Tony saw the big question mark on my face.

"I wouldn't worry, Paul. The fish you are going to eat is still alive at the time Toi orders."

We drank up and went upstairs. She ran the shower and had the towel ready when I parted the curtain. She dried and rubbed my back. It felt so good, oh yes.

Getting dressed to go out Toi turned her back towards me.

"Hey, boy. Hook braw. Yes."

Toi's "yes" most of the time meant "please."

I sat down on my bed

"Tell you what, we hook this thing later..."

With a devious smile she teased, "Yeah? What on your mind?"

I pushed her bikinis down and drew her to me.

"Paul, gân kuâi, hurry up! I'm really hungry now."

A cab took us down the WUFU to the Love River bridge. We got out and walked across. Whoever had come up with this name must have been immune to the rotten smell that escaped from it. Small tug boats were busy pull-ing short barges up and down the black water.

"Why 'Love River?' It stinks."

"Long ago young people stand on old bamboo-bridge and had love together, become man and wife. They lis-tened to Jenai Ho River, real name, telling secrets, bringing long life from mountains far away. Not any-more, too dirty."

She spoke like a child reading from a fairytale book. I squeezed her arm as we entered the restaurant. Cooler and dryer air invigorated me. The foyer was staged with illuminated saltwater aquariums on either side. Fish, long and thin, flat and oval, fat and short, played with the air bubbles that escaped from under strangely shaped rocks and large abalone shells.

"Which you like?"

"What do you mean, 'like?'"

"Eat raw, cooked, or baked."

"You ain't kidding me, girl, huh?"

Toi must have known the hostess. They greeted each other like long-time friends.

"My man eat one of fish."

Alissa—where did they get that name from?—netted two Toi had selected, weighed them, and took the bowl to what must have been the kitchen.

We entered the dining room. Cool ginger-spiced air and the soft light from lanterns ushered peace into this evening. Two beautifully dressed young ladies led us to a round table by a window, away from the Loving River. Bowing, bowing.

"Tsank a you, tsank a you."

A waiter brought a wire basket holding six ice-cold, fogged bottles. I remained rather suspicious. Toi must have felt that. She reassured me.

"You, good boy. I know you like."

The appetizers arrived in a crystal bowl filled with garlic-lemon-flavored water. Tiny live shrimps were twitching in it all over. Toi mixed soy sauce, mustard, and ginger. She caught one of those wiggling animals with her chopsticks, dipped it into the brownish brew and held it right in front of my face.

"Open, I feed, is custom. You worry nothing, okay? Is nice you here."

Her almond-framed eyes looked so sweet. I opened my mouth, though not too wide.

"You close now. Paul, you so funny."

I did. Not bad at all. Tasted rather okay. Toi waited, not sure the critter would stay down. The grin on my face made her smile.

"Good. You my man!"

The two ladies from earlier served the main course. Thank you, thank you. Even sitting I bowed. Terrific, fried fish, garnished with herbs, garlic, seaweed, and peas. The other veggies I did not recognize. Some looked like asparagus sprouts, but did not taste like them. I had to admit, heat or no heat, nowhere had I eaten any fresher and better tasting seafood!

More beer? I shook my head.

"No, thank you, woman, I still have to do some work tonight."

No fortune cookies? How come? Noticing the moderate bill I knew my dollars would go a long way. The tip I left on the table impressed Toi.

"Too much!"

She took some of the NTs off the table and put them into her purse. She offered, "Foa laetaw, Paul."

I brought her back to Westminster.

"Don't lock door, okay?"

I let the cab go and walked the short distance back to the hotel.

Past eleven, the stores were still open, the streets alive with taxis and people. The days here seemed to last from four in the morning until way after midnight with some running right into the next morning.

Sitting in my room by the window, I thought of leaving Tanya. As a good wife, she had all along taken good care of me and my son Martin. She had healed me from my drinking and had helped to sort out the last five years of my life with Rita.

"What is it with me? Is there no loyalty in me at all? How will I tell her? How can I do this without hurting her?"

When people leave each other, there always is hurt. The scars keep oozing for years to come. I will not forget Rita saying, "You break your word like children break their toys!"

One day I would have to face it and come clean without excuses. When?

Tired I went to bed, leaving the door ajar. The sound of running water woke me up.

"You, Paul, I miss. Put arm around me, love me."

And after a while the night went to sleep again.

Toi was still dreaming in my bed when Ken and I had our breakfast downstairs. The three-minute eggs were right on.

"You look different, Paul. Relaxed. Okay! We will get these gearboxes done. John from NorLine told me about you. I think I have an idea where you are coming from."

"Hey, question. Does Hsiu stay with you overnight?"

"Yes. Once in a while I slip the floor manager a few NTs. I made sure the man on your floor knows about Toi. It's okay."

Our van arrived. At six in the morning the outside temperature already sweltered around the ninety-eight-degree mark. The air was so humid I could feel it between my fingers. We were steaming before we sat down in that air-conditioned car. Mr. Chen picked us up at the gate. For the first few days the security guards went all out to keep China Shipyard safe. Not much bowing going on there. Without Mr. Chen it would have been a disaster. These security guards were highly suspicious of Americans wanting to enter their shipyard. Also, the slightest mistake they made would get them fired on the spot. Mr. Chen helped to convince them that all my paperwork was correct.

As time went on, it got better. My "tsauw an"—"good morning"—helped. The guards got a kick out of my twisted Taiwanese. It made them smile and yell, "Okay, okay! Hello, Miestaw Paawl!"

The bus took us to the repair shop. Some ten young mechanics were waiting, a clean-cut bunch dressed in blue jeans and shirts. "Made in Taiwan."

"Goot moning, Miestaw Paawl!"

Were they ever polite! I huddled with Ken and Mr. Chen and shared my thoughts regarding the problem at hand. The gearbox had been disassembled. The clutch ring showed bluish discolorations along its periphery.

"I think the overheating occurs because the oil cannot escape between the pressure plates. We should drill holes in the retainer ring to provide passage for the oil to escape."

"Well, we've tried everything else. It makes sense, though it never occurred to any of us. Let's do some testing."

We went to the outside test area. The men formed a semicircle around the setup. They were pointing, talking, seriously nodding, and whispering as if they were making the rounds with the chief resident in a hospital. Of course, I did not understand a word.

It took the rest of the day to run the tests. The evaluated data confirmed my suspicion. We decided to go ahead with the drilling. Aware of the importance to be right the first time, I wondered why nobody had thought of this before. They had been at this for nearly a year.

On the way to the hotel Ken informed me it would take at least two days before the box would be ready for another test. The plan called for me to lay out the holes the next day. Ken would stay there, and I would have a few days off.

"Is that okay, Ken? I don't think it's right for me to goof off while you are working. I don't feel good about that."

"Do you always worry like this? I bet you nothing much will happen before Friday. I've been there, believe you me. You go and see the country. Hsiu tells me Toi likes you a lot. She wants to show you around. Have at it, man!"

I called the club and told Toi I would be busy that night, but probably have some time tomorrow afternoon. Then I called Tacoma and made my first progress report.

I should have called Tanya too. I had not talked to her since my arrival here. But I didn't want to do this over the phone. She deserved better than a call. I needed, wanted to speak to her face to face.

The layout of the holes went as planned. I left the yard shortly after one o'clock. I had barely cleaned up and changed into fresh clothes when Toi showed up. I had arranged for her to have a key to my room.

"We fly to Makung Island tonight. I got ticket for us."

"Hold it, Miss Beautiful. I have to go to work tomorrow, and where is Makung Island?"

Hugging me, she slid onto my lap,

"No, Ken say you must go with me, yes. We take ship back on Thursday. Is so romantic! I make you happy. Three hours when plane leaves. Yes, yes, okay?"

All right. I had noticed she wore almost the same clothes every day.

"How much were the tickets?"

"Few NTs. You have swim pants? We go beach. Nice there. Warm ocean."

She jumped up and twirled around and around till I caught her and drowned her song with kisses.

"Girl, you are something!"

"We need shopping, come."

The cab dropped us off in the middle of town. The driver promised to wait.

"Okay, Paul. No charge."

One woman at the department store spoke English. I approached her.

"Good afternoon, we have not much time today. Please show my friend here some nice things for her to wear. And I need a pair of swimming trunks."

We bowed politely. She took Toi to a different section and waved a young fellow to help me.

My girl came back with two cotton skirts and some raw silk blouses, beige and ochre, soft pastel that matched her Michelangelo face.

"Too much, Paul?"

"No. I couldn't have picked nicer clothes. You look gorgeous, young lady."

I paid. The clerks hanging around were giggling.

"Have nice time on Makung!"

"Did you tell everybody, the whole wide world?"

"Yes. Paul, I so happy, I can't keep myself."

I wanted to know more about her, needed to find out where this air of elegance came from. Why does she work at Westminster? I needed to tell her about myself, that I am married, where I lived, and more.

During the short flight Toi told me we would go to the harbor at night and watch the fishermen prepare their skiffs for the early morning catches of squid, octopus, swordfish, marlin, and giant lobsters. I figured that would be a good time to listen and talk.

Landing on the island felt similar to landing in San Francisco. No runway, only water below. Will we make it or not? At Makung, though, a jade-toned, crystal-clear sea rippled over coral reefs that rayed myriads of color combinations from beneath the tropical ocean. Breathtaking!

The girls at Westminster had asked Toi to bring back dried squid and other fine fishy foods the island is so famous for. The old Makung marketplace, lined with shop after shop, offered the harvests sloops brought back daily from the sea. Shark teeth and fins and sharkskin, anchovies and skip jack tuna, three-foot-long bonitos, and mackerels. We shopped around for a while. Toi bought a bottle of Kaoliang, a potent liquor made from sorghum plants, a grass that grows on the island.

"For Theah, she like very much, yes?"

I bought a pair of earrings, a pearl set in red gold. The jeweler, an old man with a thin white beard, looked at us. With his head almost touching the glass on his counter, he reached for our hands.

"Long life, long life. Buddha with you."

A shiver ran through me. What did that mean? We brought the packages to the hotel and again took to the narrow streets. She took my hand as we climbed the wide stairs to the ancient temple.

"Paul, you pray?"

"Sometimes, not often enough. You know my God listens to a different name, but I am sure your Buddha knows Him or at least His father."

Who is Jesus' father? God? Joseph? It never had been real clear to me.

"We burn incense. We pray Buddha?"

"I will pray with you."

The temple boiled with people from nations all around the world. Hundreds of candles flickered in the dim twilight. I felt peace in me and bowed way down to the jade floor.

With the murmuring of all, our prayers, too, went to Buddha.

"Dear Lord, please..."

That does not fit. Why not? Would His mother do? She always had listened to me.

No, this here is not Sacré Coeur in Paris, not Notre Dame, those cold places that have seen sinners come and go for hundreds of years. The temples here in Taiwan were not like our western basilicas, where man still is paying down on Adam and Eve's debts.

Why is our "Buddha" still hanging on the cross? Who put Him back up there again? Who? They had taken Him down once on Golgotha. Had He not risen?"

The temples on these islands were warm. They gleamed with red, with jade and gold from hills above rich rice fields and terraced tea beds. They were alive with a God seemingly friendlier than the one on that cross. These temples here had no doors; open day and night to people offering gifts of rice, chickens, fruit, tea, and wine. Monks consoled the burdened ones and chanted with those who knew of no prayer.

I felt her arm around my waist, her fingers playing with my shirt.

"Come, to harbor."

I would have liked to stay a little longer, but later I would have time to think more about all this.

We sat down close to each other and right at the water's edge. Large boulders still shared the warmth the sun had left in them. The humid air tasted salty and smelled of boats and nets. Many sloops were moored to floating gangways. Some fishermen were folding their nets and others sat around smoking and passing cups of rice wine. Voices from women and children drifted across the water. Time seemed to have forgotten to move on.

The sky dipped into the tranquil sea beyond the harbor, and in the misty twilight a setting sun searched for darkness.

"Paul, after this night, you no more want me. I am not girl you think."

She looked to where the sky touched the sea. Her profile, contrasted by the twinkling lights of the wharf, burned itself deep into my mind.

"I tell after we home next day, but Buddha in temple let me know to speak now. You need listen. I ran from my home in Hsinying. My family poor. No place at farm my father has. I go to woak for money for Mama San at the club. Paul, my heart hurts. I saw you, you different from other men. You hold me like woman, not like geisha girl."

I pulled her closer. She tried to push me off.

"Paul, when we get back I will no see you anymoa..."

"Stop! Toi. Please stop!""

I took her face into my hands and kissed her tears.

For some time both of us listed to the ripples that kept playing with the small rocks along the shore. She tried to get up, but I did not let her.

"Please, Toi, listen to me. I cannot explain what is happening inside me. When I looked for the first time into your eyes I had feelings I never ever had before in my life."

It sounded so trite, a cliché stolen from a cheap story. How could I say it better, make her understand? She did not look at me.

"Men say same to me befoa."

There it was! In slow motion first, the frames then jittered into a stilled picture.

Ten years ago in San Francisco I had spoken the same line to Tanya: "I have never, ever before felt this way." Lynn, my secretary during the sixties, Knita, my friends in other cities, they all had heard that same line: "I never ever felt this way." Had I just come up with an old, smooth lie?

"Toi, believe me, please, it is not important for me to know where you come from, or what you did in years gone by. I am beginning to fall in love. You have me touch moments I thought to not be within my reach."

I felt bathed in fire. My hands held onto hers to keep mine from shaking. I just had said I am falling in love. Why did I say that? Love? But I did not stop.

"I want to take you away. Your hurt I want to soothe, this heart of yours to be free from bygone days and painful hours. I want us be together and share what we think and feel. I say this to you and I mean it."

Turned away from me, she brushed my hands from her lap.

"Let me go."

"Not yet. You need to know I am still married to a good woman back home. To be honest with you, I feel guilty, so very guilty..."

What had I just done? I sat down in the chair by the window that would be my cot for the night. Toi lay on the bed with her back to me. What was happening? I dozed into a restless night.

When I woke up, the fishermen had left the harbor already. My back hurt. I did not see Toi. Maybe she had gone downstairs? I stood up and stretched. On the small table next to the bed I found my ticket for the ferry back to Kaohsiung. A scribbled note on the backside said: "I love you too, but can no see you again." Her new clothes were folded neatly on the bed, the small velvet box with the pearl earrings on top.

The ferry found its way back to Kaohsiung. Late that evening Ken knocked and came in.

"What is going on, Paul? Hsiu called me, all upset. I asked her to come here, if that is okay with you."

"Ken, I don't know what is going on, I don't. I sure as hell wish I did..."

"Hi, Ken, Paawl."

Hsiu, fidgeting nervously with the strings of her purse, did not want to sit down. I got three beers from the small fridge in my room.

"Hsiu, what? Where is Toi?"

"Toi love you. She not hurt you. You have wife, she very sad..."

"Hsiu, where is Toi? Please tell me! Where is she? I need to see her, talk to her..."

"She with my mother. You not see her, she too sad. She say, she is not girl you can love."

I looked at Ken.

"Jesus Christ!"

To shout His name in Buddha's land bordered on blasphemy. I hoped both would forgive me.

"Will you, please, tell her I did not have a chance to explain how I feel and what I want to do about it? Here, take her things, all of it belongs to her."

Ken did not know how to act. He dared anyway.

"Paul, I'll find out. Relax. Tell me, you like her that much? You want to unhitch from your wife? You really got it deep, man, don't you? I hope you don't mind me being a little worried about all this."

"Ken, all I know is that I am tumbling among avalanches of questions I have no answers for. And, again, I might not want to hear those answers. I feel joy and guilt. Truth is, I feel very close to her. What am I to do? Do you have any idea?"

Ken looked out the window.

"No. Walking in the same shoes as you are, I don't want to hear the answer either."

We finished the beer.

"By the way, nothing is going to happen at the yard tomorrow. It is a Buddha day. Sorry, forgot to mention that the other day. The first ring is in the machine shop. How about you and I going to Kenting Park in the morning? We'll take the bus. It is quite a ride, but the southern tip of this island is very beautiful. Sleep on it and don't worry."

He held my hand longer than usually.

"Paul, Hsui and I are going to eat at a Mongolian place downtown. Would you..."

"No, thank you, I am ... no, see you in the morning."

I called room service and shortly my dinner arrived on a nicely decorated cart; fried squid and baby octopuses with rice, bamboo chutes, peanuts, and greens on the side. The waiter stashed away a good tip. These young men did not make any money at all. The hotel let them stay way up under the hot roof, had them make payments for their uniforms, and fed them with leftovers.

"Tsank a you, tsank a you!"

He bowed himself out the door. I ate, turned off the lights, and for a while stood by the window looking down onto the busy street where people like ants were moving the sidewalks.

"What am I doing to my life? I am here to fix a manu-facturing problem, a serious one at that. My head is spinning over a young woman I have known for only a few days. What is wrong with me? Is there something I do not see? Tanya, I am about to hurt her heart, which really deserves happiness and not pain. Am I that self-centered? Do only my feelings count?" It would take many years to answer that question with a regretful, but clear and honest "yes!"

"Buddha, I am in your country. I need your help, your advice and guidance. Do I dare to shoulder the load I am to take on? Do I know what I am doing? Toi will break some day. Is it up to me to keep her well, to heal her heart? Lord, do you think I am making all this up, yes? Do those great words of mine conceal my short-comings, my greed for youth? Am I kidding myself, hiding behind a false good will to cover up the truth, the truth that I am drawn to this woman because she is so fragile, so troubled, so very beautiful, and so in need of help? Answer me, please. Is it just compassion that compels me to feel this way? Do I think all this because I feel pity for her?"

"Mary, holy Maria, can you do something? But I would like your help in a special way, in a way that allows for my craving for laughter and love and pleasure. I don't think you will do that. What a fake I must be to even approach you with that. Honest now, did you put this in my way on purpose? Beyond my unworthiness, do you really ask me to make a new life for her? Yes? And undo my promise I made to Tanya?"

Ken had the bus tickets. Hsiu asked if she could come with us.

"Sure, but only if she tells me where I can find Toi."

"Toi very sad. She go home to mother in Hsinying. She need time, she okay."

What a ride! I suffered the heat, no air-conditioning on this thing. The beach stretched out like any other beach does, white sand, wide, hot. But the stinging jelly-fish and the eighty-five-degree salty surf made swimming impossible. After a few icy beers, the jellyfish did not sting anymore. They did not like alcohol-tinted blood. We sat under large umbrellas, but the burning sun got us just the same.

We took some beer along and walked through the park. After a few steps into this paradise drowning in exotic plants and wildly blossoming flowers, we saw a tarantula tending to her net, anchored to a few bonsai-like branches. Ken and I both jumped.

"You scared? She fix net. Come see, she eating big bug, look?"

"That is fine, just fine, Hsiu. Let her eat in peace."

She wanted to play hide and seek in the three-hun-dred-foot-long cave that snaked through contorted rock formations.

"Girl, it's too hot!"

But Ken ran off with her anyway. Eventually we came to the "Fairy Cave" and marveled at the Blessed Spirit

Tortoise, a huge rock shaped like a turtle with a dense growth of bushes on its back.

All along colorful birds with long tail feathers sang songs that sounded like a Skilsaw after it has been shut off. No, I am not making this up. It sounded like many carpenters trying out their saws.

Ken and I had run out of beer and energy. We were tired, but we hiked a little farther to take in that breath-taking view of the southern shoreline. Stone slabs polished by the ocean curved south toward the tip of the island. The sea had hollowed out large boulders and had trans-formed them into ancient sculptures not made by man.

The bus that brought us home had no glass in the window frames. We dozed through the long ride and were burned by the sixty-mile-an-hour hot draft.

The floor-manager seemed to be bothered by something.

"No Toi? You sad?"

He knew. Why did this not surprise me?

"Well, I hope she will come back."

I gave him ten NT.

"Tsank a you, Miestaw Paawl, okay, okay."

Ken and I had dinner at the hotel's cafeteria down-stairs. We didn't say much. The "Western Steak" was tough and the potatoes should have stayed a little longer in the steamer. But it made no difference. We decided on the schedule for the next few days, and then I went to bed.

The TV turned itself off.

Somebody sat on my bed and stroked my hair.

Hold on to that dream, don't let it go. Come, let me hold you. Please don't go away.

"Do you really mean what you say to Hsiu? You not worry what I did befoa?"

Did I hear right? Is this real? It is her "befoa." No, please don't let me wake up. Have me keep on dreaming. It feels so good. Don't, don't let me wake up...

But I did turn over and with my eyes closed I searched and found her face.

"Toi! I missed you."

"Paul, sorry, I wake you up. I want hear you say. You have Tanya. You honest man, tell me about wife. Other men lie. I can see white on finger where ring is. You did not take ring off. I knew you married. I think nothing bad to flirt and have fun time with you. Then you say, you in love, I am scared. Very sad in Makung. I worry, cannot be by you. Only few days I know you. You care. I think of you, I hear music, feel good love. I told Mama San. No longer woak in club. I go home, you come with me or not. You tell me now. Yes?"

We talked till deep into the night, ad-libbing tomorrow. Later, all cuddled up, she said,

"Paul, I am safe. It is good to have youa arm by me."

"Hey, man, good morning! Wow! Paul you look like a Polaroid picture that has been taken with a dead battery in the camera."

"Go away."

"Oh, hostile? Yeah, the sun does that to people. But I am happy for you."

"Ken, who else knows, the whole city?"

"How many times do you want me to tell you? These girls have no secrets."

Friday morning, the last day of our three-day week, the van dropped us off by the machine shop at the far end of the yard. Ken pointed at several long and tall buildings,

"They build smaller ships in those. The roofs are retractable. They have an interesting assembly schedule. It is based on a horizontal and vertical material/component supply flow. That monstrous bridge crane over there lifts and transports the finished vessels to the launch-ways."

Four young men stood by and observed the drilling.

"Ken, there are so many people standing around. They don't seem to have anything to do."

"I wondered about that myself. Mr. Chen told me the yard has a great number of apprentices who during their first year are told to be close to the work and just watch."

"Well, makes sense."

Lunchtime, not the usual siren or the eardrum-bursting lunch whistle, but a recording of the sound of the thirteen-ton Big Ben tower bell in London. Chopin at the airport, Presley in the bars, and now this! Who would have thought?

Some two thousand workers ate their lunch, drank boiled water, pulled a straw mat from under the workbenches, and bedded down.

"These are the simplest pullout beds I ever saw. How long is lunch time?"

"An hour, and music will call them back to work. Come. I asked the bus driver to get us to the executive dining room. The general manager has invited us for lunch."

Starched, white tablecloth, cotton napkins, shiny silverware, upholstered chairs, air-conditioning, and a bill of fare similar to the fancy places in town Ken had introduced me to.

"Mr. Tsao Gang, please meet Paul Berck from BayShip."

He wore the same clothes as his workers did in the yard, denim shirt, blue jeans, and safety shoes. Gray hair fashioned his lean face. He spoke his English with a slight Oxford accent.

"Hello, Mr. Berck, glad to see you here. Are we doing all the right things for you?"

"Thank you, Mr. Gang, yes. We will have these gearboxes fixed shortly. I am sorry it took us this long to come up with corrective measures."

"I need to tell you how good this sounds to my ears. What is the problem?"

Tsao ordered beer and listened intensely to my dissertation.

"Good. Give me a call, please, when you do the final testing. I might, just might, fit that into my schedule. Here is my number. Sorry I cannot stay longer today. Yes, here we have meetings too. Next week I want to tweak you about Cad–Cam. Ken spoke about it. You are using it in your engineering department?"

"Of course, but before you leave, sir, I must say I am tremendously impressed with your facility and the people who work here."

"Thank you, Mr. Berck. Call my secretary should you need anything."

We got up and bowed our goodbyes.

"What a guy, Ken."

We finished our Peking duck with another ice-cold beer.

Sharp at five minutes to one o'clock, the "Tennessee Waltz" danced through buildings, shops, along the docks and accompanied thousands of straw mats being rolled up. One had to be there to believe it.

At the Kingdom, Tony slid two frothy jugs our way.

"On the house, boys!"

Friday afternoon, not a stool left to sit on.

"Here is to you, Ken. Thank you for doing all those good things."

"Hey, I hear you are going to Sun Moon Lake this weekend."

"Well, hello, should I act surprised when the woman tells me? I cannot believe this."

"Take it easy. You see, these girls pull out all stops when they feel something nice is coming their way. For them it is like a walk through fairytaleland. They know you are not one of the usual pals western outfits send over here. Paul, I hope you don't mind me talking to you that way. I like you. You are a down-to-earth man. You've been around the block and back..."

"Yeah, I feel the same about you. How many times have you been around the block?"

"Sarcasm is not your strong side, sir. Hmm, it's always the same. Two people only, but you can bet one of 'em is a comedian."

"Let it go. What about Moon Lake?"

"Now, is this part of my job description?"

"Comedian, who? Moon Lake, go!"

"Hsiu once took me there. It is a long trip, but it is very beautiful country. Buddha made it for romantic people like the two of you. Here, I brought you an advertisement."

I fell in love with the words on the brochure: "The lake is shaped like the crescent of the moon. Its turquoise-hued waters touch the rolling foothills of the Chungyan Mountain Range."

"Yes, Paul. It is very beautiful. There are people and people and then some. They pray at a very famous temple. I am sure Toi will take you there."

"And what are you guys going to do with this weekend?"

"Hsiu and I will go to Orchid Island, Lanyu Island, about fifty miles southeast of T'aitung. We fly. It will be interesting. The Yami tribe there still practices customs that were passed on by their Polynesian ancestors. I'll bring a trinket back for you. How about a shrunken monkey head? Shark teeth on a string? Ha, have a nice weekend."

"Funnyman, go, take your medicine. I'll see you…"

"Y̶ou like hot or cold shower?"

I went for a cold one. When I finished and came out I saw another girl sitting on my bed. Toi, busy with ironing one of my new silk shirts, did not look at me.

"My friend, Theah. Take shower here? She alone on weekend. Yes?"

"Gee, surprises all the time, ha. Sure, it's okay with me."

Theah disappeared in the bathroom and took a long shower. Toi motioned.

"Come, we make love."

"P̶aul, we go to countryside, Sun Moon Lake with train and bus tomorrow, Okay?"

"Sure. I like to see your land, to meet your people. We need to talk about your rice fields and your temples. I want to listen to your music. You tell me about Confucius, your parents, and…"

"Hey, go dinner first, yes? Want eat snake? Is like chicken. Or snails, you eat snails?"

She thought I was bluffing when I nodded.

"Where?"

"In France and Italy I did. But I never have eaten snake. Theah come?"

Without noticing it I tuned into the rhythm of her "English."

"I must kiss you for that. Thank you, Paul."

We drove by Kaohsiung's night market, a busy place and open until way after midnight.

"We go here next week. I buy you shirt. You watch they make it, goes fast."

Toi and Theah found a place downtown, a tall building with five floors of large restaurants. In my traveling the world over, I had never seen anything like that! The elevator let us out on the fourth floor. Again fish tanks, but these housed snakes. They looked at me, flashing their split tongues. Otherwise nothing moved. I could not even see any of them breathe. I felt a bit woozy.

Theah picked a fourteen-incher. Toi talked to the waitress. The lazy Susan turned and beer came my way. I needed a beer! It also carried small dishes with oily peanuts, ginger, sushi with green mustard, and a crystal bowl with two black things in it.

"Toi, what in hell are those?"

"Eggs, I'll show you."

The hen had buried them in deep mud and the farmer must have forgotten for a long time to pick them up.

Theah held both hands up to her face. She could not stop laughing, but then Theah laughed a lot all the time and about anything.

"Paul, you so cute. Toi, tell him."

"Chinese thousand-year-old eggs, very good."

Right away I feared whether they might also have swallow nests, another of the more unusual Asian delights. Snake, yes, snake I thought would be okay after all.

"Paul, you good with chopsticks, yes? You bet I can pick up four peanuts?"

"Like one at a time? Are you kidding me? I can do that, too. No bet."

"No, four peanuts at one time I hold between my chopsticks."

"Really? I got to see that. Okay. 100 NT, you can't do it."

"Watch me after we eat. I win."

Toi worked on those fossilized eggs. Fortunately the place had good ventilation. The looks of them almost did me in. Black, they were black, real black.

"No kisses for a year, hear me?"

"Ha, bad for you too. We both eat, we can kiss, yes."

"No Toi, no I don't want to, no."

I had eaten dog in the prison camp, rats and beetles, but those eggs needed to go back where they came from and for at least another thousand years!

The snake rested on a long oval plate. With the head still in place, it came dressed in spices and leaves, garlic, seaweed, and steaming rice. Toi cut the head off and sliced a sliver of meat from the body, dipped it in snake blood mixed with soy sauce, and held it in front of my mouth. She had instructed me earlier to take a good swallow from the earthen cup filled with warm rice wine if I would not be able to keep it down...

It's custom, yeah.

"Chew, might be tough."

Not tough, and it could have been chicken, but it was snake. I drained the cup. Theah came close to my ear.

"You so good laetaw. Snake blood makes man."

"You better get your four peanuts going or I..."

Toi aimed a barrage of harsh words at her.

"Paul, she jealous, ha!"

The snake, the eggs, the jealousy, and the four peanuts picked up and held in one hand between two chopsticks needed a lot of beer and rice wine. After dinner we had a good shot of herb wine from Alishan Mountain.

I handed over the 100 NTs.

"How much, I do five?"

Toi had more than enough to drink. I felt no pain. Theah could hardly stand up. The clerk at the hotel called Willie, my night floor manager, and had him carry Theah up to my room. My king-size bed easily slept the three of us boozed-out people.

Early afternoon, I felt the coming of a super grade triple-A hangover. I stumbled and searched the small refrigerator for Vodka and V-8 juice. I had to hold the bottle with both of my hands, yet I spilled while I fixed me a very bloody Mary. The V–8 barely reddened the distilled mash of wheat.

That one beer at the Westminster club a couple of weeks ago sent me on a journey so deep down I would lose my will to fight it. This morning here was just a dress rehearsal.

The vodka hit me. Calmness instantly spread through my body. I felt relaxed, though my hands still were shaky. One more of those and I'll be okay. I should have known better and been more careful last night. Taiwanese plum wine mixed with beer does worse things to a person than warm sloe gin without the rocks.

Sun Moon Lake, I'll see you some other time. I fell on the bed between those two women.

Toward evening I woke up again, bathed in sweat with my heart pumping loud and heavy. Toi, tangled up in the sheets, turned to me and put her head onto my thumping chest.

"Boy, you drank too mu-hic-uch."

It took time to navigate around her hiccup.

"You make me jealous, I ha-hic-ate you. I told Theah I ki-hic-ill her."

"Did you?"

"I threw her out. She took taxi to club. Youa heart fast. I fix drink. Will s-hic-slow down."

We were out of ice cubes, and at noon I had not put the bottle back into the fridge. The warm booze shot right back out of my mouth.

Around midnight we ordered from room service steamed octopus and ginseng juice. I began to feel a little better. Willie had sent the maid to make the bed and clean the bathroom.

We took a shower, got dressed, and went out to go dancing. Later a cab took us to the Ambassador Hotel. I tipped the night clerk to let us go swimming in the pool.

A high moon made the palm trees look like they were of sterling silver. Nobody cared about us playing in the water, splashing and hugging, naked and with not a thing to worry about.

"Hey, Ken, Orchid Island? Want to tell me?"

"I want to go and live on that island. Need to rob a bank, though, first. Did you like the lake?"

"We got drunk instead, I am sorry to report. I should have stayed with Dr Pepper. I am going to screw up everything if I do not shake this. Do you know what I am talking about?"

He did not look at me when he said, "Well, let's go to work. You're okay?"

I nodded. My brain hurt as it rolled back and forth in my head.

Mr. Chen and his crew had assembled the gearbox.

"Miestaw Paawl, you push button, okay?"

The crew stood around like children in front of a Christmas tree just before the presents are opened. I pushed the starter, and after a short time, pressure gauges, thermometers, hydraulic oil flow sensors, and revolution counters told us that the "hole-fix" had been successful.

I called the general manager and gave my report.

"Good show, Mr. Berck. I'll have the yard schedule new sea trials. Keep in touch."

That afternoon I called BayShip. Mr. Huff came on the line.

"Hello Paul, I knew you'd do it. Congratulations! Take a week off after the trial and see the country. Trip is on me, you deserve it. Go have some fun..."

"Thank you, sir, thank you. Mr. Huff, Ken is a very capable man. I recommend that you let him know that."

"Okay. Have him give me a call. And, please, call me right away after the trial. Have a good day... or night, I should say."

"Thank you, sir. I'll keep you posted. Good night."

I called Ken at his room and then I tried the bar.

"Hey, Tony, is Ken there?"

"Ken here! Do you miss me? Get your ass down here. We are celebrating your fix!"

"Be there in a minute, Ken. Toi there too?"

"Man, get it. We are all waiting for you."

The floor manager caught up with me at the elevator.

"Miestaw Paawl, they have paaty foa you in bar."

He bowed down almost to the floor.

"Thank you, Willie. Thank you."

The elevator opened directly into the lounge on the second floor. At least thirty people were clapping and yelling like during a home run at the ballgame. Toi came right into my arms.

"Paul, you important man! We happy for you and Ken, so happy. Come have beer." Her English improved daily.

Hsiu gave me a big hug.

One soft lounge chair had been reserved for me. Toi lit a cigarette, and Tony brought a tall glass of that strong beer.

"To the King of China Shipyard! Wow! Wow! Wow!"

He pointed toward the crowd.

"Dear Paul, we congratulate you, but all of us here wonder what makes you tick. Please share your secret. It is beyond us to imagine how any one person can be so talented, so smart, so well-liked, so..."

"You wouldn't understand if I told you. Let's just say I was born that way."

"Hear! Hear! Hear! By Buddha, by God, he is arrogant too."

The room shook with laughter.

"Ken, let's get out of here. I'm buying dinner tonight. We'll take the girls to town, come on!"

"My black tie is in dry-cleaning."

"How will I ever again get along without your smart-assing me? Not to change the subject, Mr. Huff wants me to come home after the first trial and straighten out the engineering department. You will finish here. I told him you probably could manage that."

"Are you sure they need you, want you back? It has been running very smoothly without you, and by now for over six weeks. My sources tell me nobody there is missing you."

"Oh yeah? Be down at the desk in half an hour."

He grinned straight into my face.

"We'll be waiting for you."

We stepped into an empty elevator.

"Paul, I so proud of you. Tony say, others too, that you are very smart engineer. I am happy to be your girl."

I wore the new shirt she had bought at the night market. The tailor had sewn it while I watched. The man spoke English.

"Can you make a traditional Chinese dress for my lady here?"

"You want cheap or fancy?"

"Fancy. Here is 1,000 NT. Please, use the best materials. Yes, very fancy."

He took her measurements, and Toi gave additional instructions. She turned to me, "You man, you so sweet man, so good! You make this girl happy. I will hug you all night long."

The black silken dress, trimmed with red and golden stripes, unfolded from her shoulders on down like a windblown scarf. Shiny golden coins, sparkling mirrors, flirted with the light. White and golden tassels on her left side closed the sky-blue bandera around her slim waist. The undergarment fit very tight. I had to help her with the zipper.

"Jesus and Buddha! Toi, you look like a queen, so gorgeous! You are my queen, yes?"

She ignored the question.

"Thank you, my man. I want be nice for you and your guest. You leave soon. When?"

"Not now, girl. We'll talk about it tomorrow. Okay?"

I missed her already.

When we walked through the lobby, heads turned. The manager hurried to hold the door open and yelled for a cab. Then he started to clap and soon the people there, mostly westerners, fell in tune. Ken whistled through his teeth. Hsiu wore a red evening gown, long, trimmed with golden brocade touching her silver string sandals.

We took two cars because the girls did not want their dresses to get wrinkled befoa the evening got started. Ken could not get his eyes off Hsiu. She smiled, kissed him, and disappeared into the taxi.

As a surprise I had invited Mr. Chen and his wife. I greeted them with my deepest respect. I liked these people, their kindness and good will.

"Thank you, Mr. Paawl. We honored, we have dinner with you and Ken."

I had to force him to sit down. Ken, also dressed in a new tan silk shirt introduced Toi and Hsiu.

"No, Paul, you not sit with me. I sit with Mr. Chen and you must be next to Mrs. Chen. Is custom, okay."

Whenever Toi did something I did not see any reason for, or did not understand the meaning of, she would say those two words, "is custom," settling everything.

"Nice shirt, boss! You must be..."

"Cut it, Ken! Look at you! The embroidery is fantastic! Listen, sir, please listen. Let's do away with all that bull, please, just for this one evening, yes?"

"You really are a clown!"

The turntable, a monstrous lazy Susan heaped with exquisite foods, slowly turned; tender, fresh bamboo sprouts, pickled young ginger, a dish of diced baby ginseng root, tiny shrimps on pineapple slices floating in fish sauce, escargot in spicy butter, water chestnuts, steaming peanuts, small lobster tails, claws of freshwater crab, and baby oysters. I'm sure I have forgotten some other delicate oddities.

Toi offered those tasteful tidbits on large muscles shells; oysters bathed in soy sauce mixed with green mustard. She came around the table and with her jade-tipped chopsticks fed one to me. Burning gasoline probably tasted the same way... Jeez!

"Why you cry, my baby? Green stuff hot for you?"

"Yes, you little sweet witch, and you know it!"

The shark cheek soup tasted superb. The cook, supposedly a master chef himself, prepared the main course at a table next to us. Poached turtle meat on a bed of black beans and various vegetables interwoven with see-through rice noodles and baked seaweed. Delicious! Delicious!

Mrs. Chen marveled about the combination of this meal through Toi's animated translation of her words.

"Toi, I have never seen anything like this on any menu in our city."

"No. I put together special for us."

"Well, thank you so much. You are such a good hostess!"

The evening went on. I stayed away this time from the wine.

Unbeknownst to all of us, Ken had brought a bottle of champagne. It exploded and foam and cork hit the ceiling. Other guests cheered while Ken filled our cups.

"Paul and Toi, here is to life!"

"Thank you, Hsiu, thank you all for this wonderful hour."

Toi came over and took my hand.

The next evening I had the driver stop at the hill of Shoushan Park.

"Why, Paul? Why here?"

"You remember a few weeks ago we went up here. We wanted to be alone. Sitting on this same bench here, we for the first time touched each other's soul. Tonight Toi, I want more from you than friendship, more than making love."

She looked at me.

"What is you want, Paul?"

"I have fallen in love with you. I ask you to become my wife."

She got up and started down the trail. I followed. We walked the short distance back to the hotel. Our steps were in no hurry.

"Paul, you will forget this island and make up with youa wife. I go home, work with my father on farm. It will be hard. I think of you. You take my love. I wait. Maybe you will leave youa wife-then you come and take me to youa home. Then I will be youa wife."

4

on my way home

The flight back to Seattle had been uneventful. My guilt and euphoria spawned by my "new love" took turns tumbling through my liquor shrouded conscience. As the Boeing 747 cruised over the Pacific Ocean, it slowly dawned on me what I had done—and what I was going to do in another five hours or so. I could not think of anything, anybody I could blame for the disastrous situation I had created. I had a few more drinks and made it all go away.

The moment Tanya saw me coming through the immigration gate at the airport in Seattle, she knew. We stepped off the under ground shuttle and waited for my bags to show. Not a word had passed between us. I tried not to look at her while she searched for my face..The jetlag and the booze shielded me from the terribly sad event that unfolded in front of all these travelers probably bringing home better news than I did.

"You did not call me all that time you were over there. You are drunk, too. What happened?"

I looked at Tanya and with unbelievable calmness I said that I no longer loved her. There were tears in her eyes and for a second she seemed to shiver under my brutal words. Then she turned and walked away. I took a cab. The scene at home that followed was indescribably sad, and with my deepest regret do I look back at those days when Tanya and I said goodbye to each other. Many years later we met again and I asked her to forgive me. She did, and whenever I am up there in Alaska, we have lunch together and talk like old friends do. She always was and still is a wonderful woman.

After a few weeks Tanya left to return home up north. I began life anew once again by buying a home on the Kitsap Peninsula, north of Port Orchard. Away from the road, the house sat amidst tall fir trees and thick undergrowth. I thought Toi might like to live there with me after we got married. But things would happen in different ways.

Mr. Huff had welcomed me with open arms. If there were a medal for fixing gearboxes, Mr. Huff would have proudly pinned it on my chest.

During my absence the engineering department had further deteriorated. Many rumors along the waterfront and throughout the Tacoma tide flats told the story that our company was not doing well. Mr. Huff looked to sell BayShip, and investors on the East Coast had done some sniffing, but the stock market seemed not to know about the oncoming events. Then, one morning Mr. Huff called for a special meeting and introduced us vice presidents to the new owner of BayShip.

Within a month our new CEO, Mr. Garner, had brought his own staff on board. The executive vice president in so many words told me to go elsewhere. He gave me a severance pay check covering the amount of six months' salary, along with a letter of recommendation that far exceeded my performance record. But all this did not lessen the embarrassment of having been laid off, something I had never suffered during my career. My ego got chipped.

Since I had time on my hands, I engaged myself in trying to arrange for Toi to come to America. For unknown reasons her passport application kept being rejected. In 1982, a year after I had come home from Kaohsiung, I flew back to the island and went to the immigration office in Taipei to find out what I could do to bring her over here. While there I went to Hsinying to meet her folks and brothers and sisters; a tremendous family, good people, very, very real. All loved Buddha in their simple ways, they allowed Him to live deep in their souls.

But Toi worried me a great deal. At home she did not seem the same person I had said a melancholy goodbye to a year ago. During the two days I stayed at her father's tea farm, we did not exchange our feelings in the way we had done in Kaohsiung. At night we slept in different rooms. I felt heavy clouds drifting into my blue sky.

"Toi, why? Don't your parents know I love you and that we want to get married?"

Her answer came slowly, as if she did not want to speak the words. Her face showed no emotion, only her eyes were sad.

"A'má, my mother, and A'pá, my father, not want me to be youa wife."

Flying home on Thai Airlines, I got so drunk I passed out.

In time I got my life jump-started again, though the road, choked with boulders made out of bottles, became harder and more difficult to navigate. Loneliness greeted me at the door of my house every time I came home. I had managed to get a job at a small local boatyard doing menial engineering tasks. I showed up for work and marked my time, but my real job was to live the life of an alcoholic.

On Friday nights I went dancing at the "meat markets" along the harbor's waterfront. I still shudder at the women I let follow me home during those ugly years. Much of this had little to do with sex. Most of the time I was so inebriated I could not spell that word anyway. No, I wanted to be with somebody, and I did not care much with whom. My lonesomeness, like a cancer, outgrew my values and undermined my confidence that I would ever again find my way back from this hell that had become my home.

My whole character had changed and kept changing, until even I seemed no longer to recognize it. The alcohol kept me busy with finding ways I trusted would cover up my drunkenness. I learned how much I could drink at night and still go to work the next morning without running my car all over the road. I did not miss a day on the job. I felt as though I still had control. I told myself I could manage the situation and snap out of it later when I would not be so busy with the duties of my job. I had done it before, I could do it again. Big deal!

"I am okay, I can handle it." That sentence I repeated over and over again like an affirmation.

As the eighties progressed, my emotional and physical well-being kept deteriorating. On Saturday mornings I would get up from my sweat-soaked bed, have a drink, and lean with both arms on the sill of the half-high window in my bedroom. I'd watch the birds and maybe a deer walking by. I also saw the chunks of my broken world lying all over. My God, did I ever feel alone on Sundays. Despair and utter self-rejection rushed over me like a tsunami. After taking one more swig from the bottle on my night stand, I usually broke down and cried my heart out. Would I ever be able to shake this prison, to climb through this window and fly into freedom? I did feel in those moments the cage I had built around me, the cage with the iron bars growing thicker every day, leaving less and less space for me to see through.

And then sometime in July, 1984, around two in the morning, the phone rang. The call came from far away. Even in my drowsiness I sensed the vast distance the words were traveling.

"Paul, youa Paul? I need tell, excited, I marry to cute Chinese man next week. We have baby..."

It's no use trying to describe this moment. My voice sounded detached and strange.

"Hello? Toi?... Hello, yes,Toi. I am happy for you. I know you will be a good wife to him. Buddha bless you, I will pray. Take care..."

I could say no more, but I meant what I said. She had found someone who would make her happy, with whom she would have a family, someone who would make a home for her, help her to forget the pain of the years gone by.

The boatyard I had been working at closed its gates, and one more time I found myself on the street. I sold my house and rented a condo in Des Moines, a small town by the water, south of Seattle. From one of my apartment's windows I could see the sailboat harbor and the Home Port restaurant. The bar, crowded most of the time with people who liked to drink a lot, became my place of comfort. What a deal—I had to travel barely half a football field's walk between my home and the bar. I went there every night after work to have a couple of vodkas on the rocks, maybe three, but not more. Fridays and Saturdays, though, were different. I helped the bartender close the place.

At the beginning of 1986, I managed to stay mostly sober for a couple of weeks. I applied at the ACME Manufacturing Company in Renton, Washington, for a job in manufacturing engineering.

I really tried not to drink for a while, but I found it extremely difficult to stay off the horse and just walk behind the wagon. So, I changed that and spent the evening again with my pint of vodka.

Professionally, though, I could run circles around that engineering crew, going up the stairs any time before noon presented quite the challenge. Two flights, I needed to hold on to that railing and pause to get my breath back without attracting the attention of other stair-walkers.

When the plant services manager retired, Mr. Bucholtz, our general manager, called me to his office. He had known me since the days NorLine had done jobbing for the plant, mostly tool machine work.

"Paul, you think you can handle that services manager job?"

Yes! Wow! I did not have to think twice about that. Forever will I be thankful, forever will I be obligated to Mr. Bucholtz. This job would save me from going under, though not right away did I quit drinking. To the contrary I got worse.

By the end of 1989, the corporate headquarters in Redmond closed the Renton division. Miraculously I kept my job and became integral to the environmental cleanup of the industrially contaminated site the plant had been operating for nearly a hundred years.

I had a ball doing that job. The environmental contractor and I worked well together with the company's top management backing me up 110 percent. My paycheck kept growing.

"I must be doing something right, yes," I told myself.

My illness progressed to the point where I felt being drunk all the time made me perform even better. How I got away with that, how nobody knew about all of this remains a mystery to me. There is a chance, though, "they" did know about it, did smell the second-hand booze leaking by the Listerine I consecrated my mouth with every morning. My functioning on the job must have fooled them.

"Yeah, he smells like he drank last night, but, man, he sure is on top of things. "A drunk? Him? Really..."

Something like that might have gone around in people's mind. Maybe that's the reason why nobody said anything to me. It was unbelievable how this alcohol took care of things. It led me to believe that all was okay. And denial inside me seconded that belief time and again.

I had established some rules. No longer would I drive when I had been drinking. I would not knock off more than a pint of vodka on week nights. I would be allowed just one big swallow from the bottle between the liquor store and my apartment. Tough, yes, but I stuck with it, which only goes to show how ruthless alcohol really is. It let me make these rules to manage my drinking, to fool me into thinking I was in charge, to make possible my continued support of my habit. By allowing me to cut down on consumption, the booze had dug deeper into my system, conning me into believing that I had control over it. But I was a willing dupe.

One night at the bar, I celebrated a tremendous triumph at work. That afternoon we had successfully prevented contaminated groundwater from leaving the property, derailing the extremely harsh consequences of such a leak. I did not have to be sad or depressed to get potted. No, any event gave me a good reason to get loaded. For me that evening, happiness opened the bottle quickly. As it happened, a lady sat down on the bar stool next to me. We talked about the weather, the mayor of Seattle, and what plans I had for dinner that night.

She became, I want to say, my girlfriend—but that would be misleading. I rather felt as though I had been taken into custody by a person who uses others to make herself feel comfortable. But I fell for it, and she moved in with me. After a while I found myself paying her bills. She drank, too, but nothing like I did. To her credit, she often asked me to cut down.

Most alcoholics are very inventive, and I was no exception. I had arrived at that stage where I began to hide my bottle. Still today I cannot understand why I did that. Fay caught me the first time around. She found my fifth on top of a kitchen cabinet. Arriving home from work one night, she held it in front of me, unscrewed the lid, and poured the liquor onto the carpet of my rented apartment for which I paid dearly every month. An evening without Smirnoff would be an unthinkable situation! Fortunately, I had a few pints stashed in the trunk of my 16 valve Geo Storm sports car. That went fine for a while until the carpet episode had a rerun.

"Paul, you are sick. You need help!"

"Me?"

"I called your insurance company this morning. They said for you to go to Tacoma and apply for admission at the ADAPT outpatient treatment center. You..."

"Hey, woman, you're not my mother. How dare you..."

"Shut up! You and I have an appointment tonight with a counselor there. If you don't go with me I'll smash up the treasure you have parked in the garage downstairs. Let me also tell you, searching the trunk of your car last night, I found the two bottles you had hidden in the empty space under the cover of the back up lights. You are not sick, man. No, you are out of your mind!"

For all of that, I sure felt unprepared. I, me, coming out and admit to a stranger I am a boozer? Counselor, that sounds like I am crazy or something. I am not mentally ill. No, I am okay. Why does she want to destroy the good relationship we are having? She lives here for free and does not have to go to work. It's she who needs a counselor, yes!

"Get dressed, we're going."

"Fay, what's with that beer bottle? A little something for while we are underway? You are a drinker too. So why pick on me? And if I am not going, then what?"

"Paul, baby, that's the moment this bottle will undo your windshield downstairs. I mean it!"

I did go with Fay to Tacoma that evening and met my counselor, Sharon. Pardon me for saying it this way, but she pissed me off right from the start.

"Paul, you have to..."

Who is she? Just who does she think she is? Nobody is telling me what I can do and what I have to leave alone.

"Sharon, will your outfit tell my boss about this outpatient thing? And you are sure I have to come here five nights a week and also go to AA? I am a busy man. You know how much time that takes?"

"Get used to it. If you want help, we will show you how you can get a life. But if you don't mean it and think you are okay and don't need us, pack up your ass now and get out of here."

That impressed me. Later Sharon and I became good friends. But later means much later after I had hit bottom, and that did not happen during or right after my treatment.

I patched things up with Fay, but it did not last long and we split. She came on too strong for my taste. But it remains the truth that her getting me to that center eventually paved my way back to sanity.

With the counselor we were fourteen people in the class, from all walks of life. Women and men, younger and older, sat in a circle facing one another.

The night came when I had to read out loud in front of my classmates, telling where I came from and where I planned to go. Risking that the following may be repetitive, I would like to share what we called:

My First Step—September 8, 1990

> *… The person on page 373 in the Big Book could have been me. All I needed to do would be to copy his story and be done with it. I probably could have faked you into believing me.*
>
> *But no, I want to tell you in my own words. Kindly listen, please, let me talk about the dark hours the booze had lured me into. This is my first step.*
>
> *I know that the alcohol is well on its way destroying me…*

I kept reading about the war, the prison camps, my coming to America, my career, and how I got acquainted with bourbon on the rocks.

> *… I began to neglect my family. Silently my four children asked with their big sad eyes: You are drunk, why?…*
>
> *… Two years after I had left my family of some twenty years, someone close to me suggested that I might have a problem with alcohol. I lived in*

Alaska then. I handled blackouts routinely. How did I get home last night? Who cared?

Three years into my second marriage I quit and stayed sober for seven more years. Seven happy years... I had made it! Not so. One day smoking a cigarette, I took that first drink again. Did I really have a problem with alcohol? Naw, I can quit whenever I want to, did that once before.

I had to stop reading, my voice gave out. Sharon got up, came over and laid her hands onto my shoulders.

"It's okay, take your time."

I nodded, calmed down, read on.

I had a very responsible job, high exposure, demanding, and yet by that time I drank vodka straight without ice. It hit me faster that way, kicked me harder. I liked that. Living by myself helped; I no longer had to hide my bottles. I remember how hard it had been to keep track of all the places I had stashed-away pints. Fay often found a hidden bottle and confronted me...

I wanted to quit, I told her, but I did not mean it. Way inside me I knew I really did not have a problem...

In the morning my hands were shaking so badly that I did not dare to take them out of the pockets in my trousers. By noon I usually came

around and could walk to the upstairs offices with-
out having to hold onto the handrail.

Fay, my girlfriend, kept pushing. Why not try
this here? You people should know I came here
with an escape hatch in my bag. I always could
say no, wouldn't have to come here anymore.

But I've changed my mind. I'm saying yes...

I don't want the alcohol any longer to manage
me. I discovered something I never knew existed
in me: an urge to share my feelings with you,
and to admit that I need help. I hope you will
accept me as I am. Thank you.

That night I had spoken from the bottom of my heart.
I had meant every word I had said.

But weeks later, three-quarters of the way through
the course, I again betrayed myself, the women and men
in the circle, and my counselor. I had a bottle under the
seat of my car and drank from it on my way home to Des
Moines. Nobody noticed. The next evening at the class
my breath did not smell of alcohol. All of us had to take
a breathalyzer before the class started. It showed not a
trace. And a trace of a trace would have been enough to
get kicked out of the rehab center. So, I kept doing it. I
graduated from the clinic with flying colors, yet as a trai-
tor, a thief, and a very sick person.

"... Hi, I'm Paul. I am an alcoholic..."

That is a short sentence. But by God did I have a hard
time saying it out loud and in front of so many people. It

took me time to understand it. It took me much longer until I meant it.

Nowadays, I let everyone know when asked at a restaurant whether I would like a glass of wine or a drink before dinner.

"No, thank you. I am a recovering alcoholic."

Some waiters clap, others blush, not knowing how to reply.

I did not like to go to those AA meetings. They depressed me. People did not much talk about tomorrow. I listened to the women and men retelling their stories over and over again. Sad, very sad, they told of loneliness beyond comprehension, despair, guilt, and mutilating pain. Souls, begging for forgiveness, wanted so very much to undo a horrible past. And as soon as my treatment ended I stopped going there. I know AA meetings are the mainstay for so many alcoholics. It helps them to keep living in recovery. But those meetings did not discourage me from drinking. Right after the meeting I would get the bottle from under my seat in the car to calm me down.

I did not need ice cubes anymore. I drank it as warm as the day made it. More often now I played with the thought of ending this terrible situation. At that time I looked for a wonder drug that would make me well, or for someone who would make me quit. Taking my own life began to surface as a viable option. Why did simply quitting the bottle not occur to me? Sharon had told us alcohol is very cunning. She also had made it crystal clear that this illness is terminal. But being inebriated to the gills shuts down sound reasoning and any initiative to change the present status. Certain neurons no longer fire at all.

One night a "friend" of mine in Gig Harbor invited me to a birthday party for his wife. I got there half lit, and soon he asked me to leave. I went to my car, but could not find the key. Somebody must have taken it from my coat. I remember getting very angry, which recently seemed to happen more and more often. I took the pint from under the seat and walked away. I kept on walking some three miles until the Narrows Bridge came into sight. I stopped at mid-span. The strong wind already had torn off my expensive leather cap I had worn ever since Alaska. The cold air sobered me a little. I looked down at the tide's rushing black waters.

What if I jump? Who would miss me?

Yeah, and if they ever found me, who would even come to my funeral?

I had lost contact with my children. They were ashamed of me, their father. Though this loss was a terribly sad and severe crisis, the alcohol kept dimming my reality. I had no friends left. Only Tommy, my second son, here and there sent a card to me. I noticed his messages had become even more slurred than mine. Once in a while he called in the middle of the night, drunk and crying. But me being only half there, I did not hear his echoing, heartbreaking cry for help. Within a year he would be dying of alcoholism.

Tommy had his own band in Memphis, Tennessee. His music meant his life to him. He wrote and recorded many songs. Listening to some of them today shatters my heart. His music and lyrics cry for help, so loud, and in so many ways. Why did I not listen? Why did I not hear that?

Standing on the bridge in this tearing wind, I thought of him and wondered if he would miss me. I saw Kate's face in the distance and Toi waved. I remember screaming, throwing my arms up in the air, wildly gesticulating at the passing automobiles. I hollered at those cars, thinking one would stop and take me to where I would be warm. But the passengers must have figured I was having fun and wanted to share my laughter with them. Not one stopped. Some rolled their windows down and cheered me on. The chilling night soaked my clothes and gnawed on my bones. All of me turned numb. I walked and yet I did not feel it. One more time I leaned way over the railing and tried to fathom this yawning depth below me.

I did not know then and still today have no clue how I got back to my car. Suddenly I heard people talking to each other. I looked around to find what they were shouting about.

Me?

"Oh my God, he is back, he is here! Look, no shoes. His face is bleeding. He must have fallen into the ditch. His clothes..."

I found the key in the ignition and I drove home. My face hurt, so did my back. "I did not jump, ha, I did not jump." It began to sink in. I wondered what it meant to "hit bottom." If this night did not count as "bottom," what would?

The next day I did not go to work, but called in sick. That, too, happened more often as time went on. Not showing up for work—only a few times had I done this in my whole career, and then only because I had been ill. Without realizing it, I got close to losing it all. The alcohol had finished locking me up. I cannot say this too often: The booze let me, made me think that I kept making the right decisions. It airbrushed my image in the mirror, and I believed it. Yes, so help me, I believed it. Never mind my ever-faster beating heart and my complete withdrawal from all social contacts and events. All that did not weigh in.

At my job I did great. Governmental agencies had come to trust me. The contractor never challenged my planning. Our company's president often called me to get firsthand data on the progress we were making. The VP under whom I worked directly told me I was doing well. I made excellent money and I can say that the crew and I worked together very efficiently. We were a good team. So? No problem, right?

"No problem." Again and again this kept ringing in my ear like an endless tape.

Christmas Eve, Tuesday, December 24, 1991, I went to the corporate offices in Kirkland and picked up my bonus check. My boss also handed me a letter from the executive vice president praising our work in Renton.

Back at the site in Renton, we had agreed to shut down right after lunch. Ernie, the contractor's superintendent, and three of his foremen had pizza in my office and we exchanged a few gifts. Ernie presented me with a fifth of Tanqueray Sterling Vodka the owner of the firm, Mr. Stevens, had brought back from a recent trip to Moscow. I had never allowed liquor at any construction site I ever supervised. As much as I wanted to share some of this rare liquid, we decided to leave the cork in place. And a few hours later at home this smooth exquisite elixir would do me in but good.

"Bottom" came in sight.

The year before, I had moved my stuff into an apartment in Burien. From my window I could see airplanes taking off and landing at SeaTac. A little noisy at first, but I got used to it. Airplanes always will take a little of me with them to wherever they will land. Frequently, particularly on weekends, I would see two planes taking off very close together. It took me a while to understand that I had double vision. This phenomenon established the absolute limit of my intake for that night or day. Within minutes after those sightings I would pass out.

On my way home to my apartment that afternoon on Christmas Eve, I stopped by the liquor store on Harris Avenue and bought three one-gallon jugs of regular Smirnoff. It would be a long four-day weekend, and I wanted to be sure I had enough to drink. On Christmas Day, people like myself suffered from lonesomeness on the double.

The cooking I had already done earlier in the week. At the grocer around the corner I picked up a few incidentals and a small wreath with a beautiful red ribbon. I hung it on my door. Merry Christmas!

Daylight... I felt very cold. The kitchen smelled awful. With great effort I tried to open my eyes. With one staying shut, I saw myself lying on a floor littered with broken glass. At first I thought I was dead, and that I lay there between hell and heaven. But my legs and arms worked. I dragged my awful-looking body into the hallway. I could not move my fingers. My hands had fallen into a coma-like sleep and felt as though they did not belong to me. I had to turn over onto my side so I could look up at the wall where my phone used to hang. If I could have, I would've dialed 911. But that slight movement sent me into a spin that must have lasted for hours, because it was dark when I came around again. I found myself lying on my bed, completely naked. The tremors were incredibly strong. My pillow showed large red spots. I bled from my nose and felt pain all over. That's how my Christmas Day, December 25, 1991, ended.

"No more!" I heard my hoarse voice saying it many times over, and I still can hear it. The weekend passed. I emptied all the bottles down the sink and went to work on Monday, the first day of the rest of my life.

It took all of me and then some to stand by my promise of "No more." I said these two words a hundred times a day if I said them once. God, those were hard, hard weeks and months, some of them worse than the bad hours in the prison camp. But I noticed some improvement in my steadiness. And then the world collapsed one more time, blown apart by hurricanes.

One Wednesday afternoon in the Spring of 1992, we had just dug a deep hole where the machine shop used to be. At a fifteen-foot depth, the groundwater carried an oily sheen. As the crew worked on rigging up a pump, my cell phone rang.

"Hey, Vati, how are you?"

"Tommy? What's going on? You sound like you have a cold or..."

"I'm not feeling too good. A bad cold has gone into my lungs."

"Did you see a doctor?"

"Yeah, he says I am dehydrated a little. They will fix that in no time. I am on the way to the hospital now. My girlfriend is taking me."

"Tommy, how..."

"Vats, don't worry. It's no big deal. I just wanted you to know. Gotta go. I love you."

Those words were the last Tommy would ever speak to me. The following day a doctor called. Tommy suffered from alcohol poisoning. His withdrawal symptoms were so severe the critical care unit had to completely paralyze him. If I wanted to see him still alive, now would be the time to come.

A day later I touched his warm hands and kissed him. The last few days in his life he spent in the intensive care unit at a hospital in Memphis, Tennessee. He left us in May, 1992. We brought him back here and laid him to rest in a cemetery north of Seattle.

This happened longer than ten years ago. Sometimes I bring flowers to his grave but not often. Plucking dandelions from the flowerbed in my back yard, I sometimes still cry. And when I ride my bike down by the river, I sometimes still cry. Writing down these lines here, I am crying.

> *It is hard to stay behind while you are gone. There is still so much to do, to hug, to hold, to care, to say.*
>
> *On the grass I lay next to your grave. I shed tears 'til deep into the night. Where are you? Will I ever see you again?*
>
> *I thought I would heal, could understand. I reasoned and I prayed. To forget I even tried. Years went by and nothing, nothing changed. It still is hard, so hard to have you gone.*

I retired in 1994. Two years later Dr. V., my urologist, who I have known for almost twenty years, diagnosed me with prostate cancer. I always had been afraid of this word. Now I had cancer growing inside me, and beyond my control. Dr. V. cut the gland out. He did a marvelous job. Everything went as planned.

"Doctor, I do trust you will do the best you can. I feel safe with you."

"Paul, I will operate on you as I would on my father..."

It took me a while to recover, but after a year or so I had all my strength back. I know now that, once we harbor cancer, we will stay its host for the rest of our lives. We become survivors and we have to do all that is in our power to keep surviving. I am taking medicine to make sure that those weird cells remain in a deep coma. No, it never will go away, not either will my uncertainty ever disappear or my nervousness before I learn about my semi-annual test result.

This cancer adjusted my values. The essence of my life once again came into focus. I really began to understand that this "I will do it tomorrow..." no way is cutting it. I have known for a long time that I cannot change the past. Yes, though never before did I really see this tomorrow as a gift that I may not be able to collect. I have only "now" to deal with. This moment I am alive and at no other time will I be able to share my good will, forgive, help, and love.

Throughout all these years I did not know for sure what it meant to have peace in me. I equated it with feeling good, with being elated. But then I came to understand that peace is not an event, not a mood. Peace is an ever-blooming flower, not given freely or lightly, but rather obligating me to live with all the intensity I am capable of. Yes, this cancer helped me change into a more tolerant person. I discovered that there is much more gray living between black and white than I ever thought I could accept.

For the last three years I have been working as a trained volunteer phone worker at the Seattle Crisis Clinic. I thought I knew about life, about living at the edge, about despair, about having no hope. But I learned I only knew very little. Matter of fact, I had no clue!

My work at the clinic enriches me, lets me see how unimportant my own story is in comparison to those women, men, and children who no longer can execute their options. I think I found an explanation for my addiction to alcohol. When did it start? Why did I fail so many times in trying to stop? I believe it has been with me all the time. And, unbeknownst to me, some event switched it on. My ignorance prevented me from doing something about it when it would have been so very easy to change the pattern.

It is now the summer of 2003, years have passed. Every morning I ride my bike along the river. My life could hardly be more beautiful. I am in love, so new and so precious. And peace is living with me.

My children, Rob, Martin, and Jessica, have become my friends again. I went to each one of them and asked for forgiveness. I asked them to join me in rebuilding our relationship. I am very thankful I had time in my life for this to happen. Because I know without peace, without love, nothing can grow.

Once in a while I even talk with Shatty. Remember my shadow? Here and there I flinch listening to its critique of my meandrous reporting. Shatty would scold me.

"Paul, you are hedging. Tell it all. Don't just deliver bits and pieces that shade the truth..."

"Well, Shatty, I don't want people to get bored. And anyway, who said I would tell it all this time around?"

"Ha, I knew it! Nothing has changed. You still are not getting it."

"You might be right. Maybe I never will, but..."

Part II
I keep writing

I keep writing…

Short stories and a few poems you will find written on the pages that follow. Paul Berck's ventures have come to an end. It's no longer fiction from here on out, but real moments in my life allowing you to see how, over time, I kept becoming who I am today. As Claus, I finish, what for now, is left to tell.

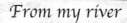

From my river

these my greetings today are wrapped
with sunshine bright and warm
the ribbon is blue borrowed from the
sky stretching far beyond my town

please let me share with you this beautiful
morning so soft so tranquil so filled with love
let me share this precious
moment of peace

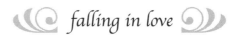 *falling in love*

River! River, stop flowing, please, and listen.

You need to know. I want to share.

I have fallen in love, yes. She is so very beautiful. Her voice is music. I believe she thinks like I think. Only for a short while, a few hours, have I known her.

You? You, have fallen in love? I am so happy for you! By the way, I have to keep moving, so you better start walking with me. Say, what's her name, where does she live, how did you…?

River, that is not important right now. I hardly know how to spell her name. But I feel joy way inside me. An elegant woman she is, soft, almost fragile, but so very gracefully does she walk.

Hm, I've known you for many years. You falling in love is something I would not have thought ever to happen again to you. I thought you had become a loner, and happy at that. What got into you?

Don't know. Did not see this mighty wave coming at me, no. I looked into her eyes and saw a radiant reflection of a soul so pure, so colorful, so longing for love. Her hands, too, told me the same, somewhat ascetically, yet giving and wanting at the same time. Hands of artists are that way.

Tell me, you are still walking on this earth, yes? I have never seen you like this. Does she know you love her? Is she alone? Did she...?

Well, I wrote to her, talked over the phone—but, no, I do not think she knows how deep my feelings are. No, I don't think so.

What if? She might not want your love. She might already be loved by another man and maybe more. How deep then will you fall from the cliff you now are sailing high above?

River, I've been thinking about that. But you see, this love of mine is different from what I understood it to be a long time ago. It is not so physical as then. It's deeper, not so much wanting, but giving abundantly...

I'm hearing nothing new. It would hurt you, it...

River, river, be calm. Daring, I hope I will never stop to dare. And should time come when my love for her is not accepted, I will come back to you and ask to take my tears to the ocean where they will find others I have wept before.

July 18, 2002

a beautiful morning

The air is crisp. The blue sky drifts puffy clouds. Frost has whitewashed the green grass in my yard. The roofs of my house and the other ones across the street have white shingles. They glitter in the early golden sun.

I am listening to soft, very beautiful music. Enya is singing,

Angels answer me, are you near if rain should fall? Am I to believe you will rise to calm the storm?

Every day when light breaks through my windows I am asking that same question. And an answer comes to me. Good feelings settle in my room and in my soul. I marvel how fortunate I am. It is warm here in my house. I'm not hungry, and there is plenty food on my cupboards. No aches bother me. My mind is clear, and my hands still can do good things.

What a life!

Today is one of those mornings that let me feel how immense our world is, how small I am, and yet how important it is that I walk it tall and straight. Moments like these are gifts from a heaven so endless, so radiant with light. Moments like these become my tomorrow.

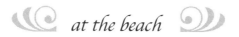 *at the beach*

Seahurst shoreline, it's a little to the west of Burien where I live.

I often go there, sit on a drifted log and listen to the silence. Small waves wash ashore, and seagulls draw their piercing cries far over the water. A soft wind touches my face as it sweeps down along the beach.

I doodle in the sand with my finger or with a piece of bark the tide had left. Flowers I draw, circles, straight and crooked lines and funny faces.

Heedful of my soul and of those who sat here before, I think of God and what I need to do tomorrow. There is music in me.

Mighty, majestic sounds overtone the beat of my heart.

Gulls, waves, wind, silence, and clouds, harmony.

Ebbed waters wait. Currents stand still. The seaweed does not sway. Barnacles close their shells. Not far off, twisted kelp floats without motion. The Sound is sleeping. Its face is that of mirrored glass.

But the beach is crawling with life. Clams spit straight up.

Small crabs hurry, crisscross the grainy sand. Birds are all over.

A new tide is being born.

Undone will be the tracks I made. The things I drew will fade into the sand. Waves will flatten this canvas for me to scribble on again, next time I come here to pray.

Summer, 2001

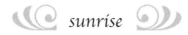 *sunrise*

At times when I am searching for the purpose of the day that just is handing back its light to the sun, I find no answers. At times when my backyard becomes my world, and I think my town is the only city where all the people live, I feel lost like a stray bee not having made it back to the hive.

My lawn is dry and brown. Squirrels are digging up my flower baskets and snails eat up my garden.

I become lonely amidst my friendly neighborhood, and I worry what tomorrow might bring.

And then a new tomorrow came.

With the strike of lightning my coop burst into a thousand splinters. Deafening thunder shattered the cuffs I had locked around my wrists. The walls of my room gave way to bright light, blinding all shadows. Rain drenched my grass. The fence around my yard was gone.

I felt no borders any longer.

Free! I embraced the vast beauty of this earth. I took my motorcycle and traveled east following the mighty Columbia River. Passing Leavenworth, Lake Chelan stretched northerly to my left, as I was heading for Brewster. The wide highway narrowed into pavement curving through apple orchards. Grazing horses lent their grace to pastures along the way. Here and there fields of golden-ripe grain swayed with the wind.

My friends live near Malott, some two hundred fifty miles away from my home. They had invited me to stop by some-time this summer. Gary's home crowns a mountain high up in the Okanogen range, and far from any road.

Next morning after a dreamless night I woke way before sunrise. The stars faded into a black-blue dawn. To the east a purple ribbon, trimmed with gold, laid on top of the sleeping mountains.

I sat in back of the house and listened to the breeze. It made the needles of the pine trees whisper to the heavens above. The swishing winds ebbed and swelled, carrying music, dis-tant chords from times past eons ago.

Fragrances of dewed soil, dry grass, pinecones, and the canyon's sagebrush drenched the air.

Yes, I felt the planet moving as it dipped into the rising sun. A burst of golden fire blinded my sight. Long shadows wak-ened on the backside of hills nearby and yonder.

Birds, fluttering silhouettes against the pink sky, greeted this day, so virgin, so new, so promising. Blue jays sat on the line Mary had stretched between two trees to dry shirts and other wash.

I thought of myself so very small and not essential to the moment that surely would have taken place without me. And yet I felt a part, belonging to this earth, engaged in life, very free, and strong.

Jarred by the mightiness of the hour, ringing with joy, I asked the wind to carry my greetings, and my wishes to the people at home in my city. I prayed for those who no longer could see what I saw, no longer could hear what I heard. With the ones in wheelchairs I asked the breeze to share its scent, and with the ill in hospitals and cancer wards.

After a hearty breakfast Mary would not let us go without, Gary took me further into his pine tree mountains. A narrow footpath branched from the trail and led to a homestead the first settler in the area had claimed. Only a few weather-bleached logs tell where his home once stood a hundred years or so ago.

"The family lived here in one room. His wife gave him nine children. Over there, you see, was his cellar where they kept the meat and the milk from the cow that grazed nearby. The garden grew where we are standing. A creek runs a little up the path. To get water they had to climb down and up some hundred feet. And in the wintertime, I guess, they must have melted snow for their cooking and drinking."

Gary stopped talking. Gazing he did not move, neither did I. Silence arrested everything around us.

After awhile he then turned to me and said, "You know, Claus, I come here once in while to think of the past. Imagine how long it must have taken them to fell trees and hew the logs to build their home. Who helped his wife when her child pushed, ready to leave the womb? You know without them we would not be…"

I did not need a cathedral with colored rosettes. No one needed to play the organ for me, direct the choir. No candles and myrrh—this moment was so simple, so down to earth, so real that nothing could have made it more holy, more pure, more tranquil and closer to God.

It is not that often that peace is so near I can touch it.

peace

from my granddaughter Kati when she was four

 the old house

the old house leans
with the wind.
I feel sad.

giggling though
and laughter—
children still around?

old songs I hear
my mother used
to hum.

the floor rotted.
the windows, the front
door no longer is there.

we had chickens and a
dog in the back where
the windmill was.

I remember the storm
that took the blade
way down the road.

the breeze no longer bellows
our sheets on the line
between the fence and hutch.

blackberries and ivy now
hold up the shed where
I had my bicycle stored.

the room up there
in the loft used to be mine,
a very safe and cozy place.

so many years gone by.
no shingles are left on the
rafters and grass is growing
on the ledge.

the old house, built well,
to me it seems still sturdy
and strong.
yet I know, yes it is gone.

spring

It is happening!

The river runs higher. Its waters bring silt from the mountains down to the lake. The mornings sometimes are foggy. And yes, it still is cold.

Folks telling winter to leave, louder every day.

I am always astounded how sudden spring starts doing its thing. Over-night almond trees burst into bloom. Their lavender blossoms, pink and white, dress the trees on both sides of the street I live on. Out of nowhere yellow forsythia springs to life, beaming suns from behind fences and dotting the embankments along nearby highways.

The branches of my maple tree wear green, oblong buds. Any day their wrapped new leaves will burst into the open. The daffodils surprised me. Getting out of my car yesterday, I saw their yellow stars on the right side of my driveway. A bunch had pushed through the maple leaves fall had packed there. For a while they must have been blooming unnoticed among my green cedar bushes.

And then there is that fragrance spring sprays into the air. The wind drifts it into nooks and niches all around the city.

Something else lets me know sunnier days are coming. My feelings are softer. Now, when I ride along on my bicycle, I am looking at the sky more often. Not so much any longer are my eyes searching the ground.

I cherish this time.

New life is rushing in. It is so beautiful.

I want hold it in my hands, bring it to you and share it, so you, too, may touch these bright moments, even if you do not have a garden or cannot walk the trail.

There is a blind woman
in town.
Her name I do not know.

She gets around
feeling each step
with her white cane.

Her dark raincoat
is always open,
sailing in the wind.

A brown leather satchel
tangles from her shoulder
as she walks.

The other day I saw her
halted between a parked car
and the hedge along the
sidewalk.

Someone should help! I ran.
She brushed me off, softly:

"Thank you, no."
 "OK, take care."

How is it to be blind?

Not to see light,
not ever to know
how a flower looks,
never to see a smile,
not to see the sky,
the clouds,
only to hear the river,
never to see trees,
fall,
snow
or spring.

How is it to be blind?

Not to see the face in the mirror, in a
pond rippled by the evening's touch.

There is a woman in town.
She is blind.

I don't know her name.

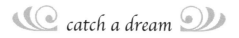 catch a dream

catcher catch a dream for me!
keep away
monsters, ghosts, and fog,
evil witches' brew,
slither snakes and
crawling critters,
ugly frogs and spider webs,
thunder, storm, and fire.

catcher catch a dream for me
from meadows, brooks
and valleys. bring elves and birds,
whisper winds and flowers,
suns and angels, violins and heavens.

catcher catch a dream
with love and passion,
life and peace.

catch it, please, for me!

Amber,

You probably get asked enough as to how you are, how you are doing and how you are taking it. So, I'll skip all that. I know you are doing the best you can.

I found that often I did not want to answer I am fine, OK, yes, it's going… I wasn't fine and it was not going. It was not going for sure the way I needed it to go. And by the tone of their voices I could tell that they really did not want to know. They were hurting, but didn't want to show it.

They were scared. I understood. I had these thoughts on my mind one time or another: "I hope I don't have it. I hope I'll never get it."

Cancer is an ugly word.

You are right, school is not over with at graduation. Some-body keeps handing out tests. The grades are held in a folder I do not have the password to.

Sometimes I got sloppy reading the questions and my answers failed the target by miles. But then it dawned, and life got a hold of me again. I had to peel away the crap. I had to scrub my soul. The shortcuts I had invented I deleted. And the old values came in sight again.

I found a set of very simple priorities. This time they did not come chiseled in flagstones. Instead they were scribbled at the bottom of my list I usually take to the grocer.

"Live Paul," it said, "accept it, live now! Forgive yesterday."

Who ever gave that message to me meant it. It took a while to sink in. But it did, and I started to run with it. The do-it-yourself-Claus finally began to do just that. And through all my pain I took charge. In time I came to understand that only I, yes, only I can make me well again.

I know you also are rewriting your shopping list. Take a pen with weatherproof ink. Mornings like this one tend to wrinkle the paper. Tears smear the letters.

Hang in there. You will make it!

I pray for both of us and for the many others who live with this ugly word that forever rewrites itself.

You need help? Let me know.

Many greetings,
Claus

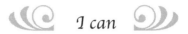 *I can*

I could have — yesterday is gone.

I will — tomorrow may not show.

I can now love you life and care.

I can smile, laugh, and weep, and

I can help.

   Yes today,

      now, I can.

 *Becky*

I miss you   in my despair
you touched me
and my soul

I miss you   in my loneliness
you spoke to me
and stilled my tears

I miss you   in my fear
you hugged me
and made me calm
you kindled me
for yet another morning

I miss you   you really cared
like no one ever did

I miss you yes I do

To my nurse at the Eastside Hospital,
who helped me not to die. Summer, 1998

my dog

my dog
> I had to let you go
>> yesterday

my dog
> I had to send you
>> far away

my dog
> my buddy
>> you were so ill
>>> your health was
>>>> nearly gone.
>>>>> no herbs could
>>>>>> make you well

my dog

    I saw you shake

        searching I looked

            into your eyes

                and held you tight

                    you shivered

                        short of air

my dog

    I had to let you go,

        and send you far

            to where your

                heaven is,

                    so you can run again

                        play and bark

                          and bark

my dog...

For Mary and Gary, August 2000

 Hello June

I have been up north, and spent a few days with my family in Anchorage. We drove to Nilichik. Awesome scenery: Mount Iliamna and Redoubt, the northern icecap beyond. We rode the train along the Susitna River between Talkeetna and Hurricane. Beavers, eagles, and moose; bears, glaciers, streams, and wilderness—all in the colors of autumn, bathed in pure gold, untouched.

All this mightiness is so unspeakably beautiful!

I felt small, so unimportant and yet I was, still am, part of this majestic world torn to and fro by currents and riptides of untamed waters—Cook Inlet and Turnagain Arm, carved by ice long long time ago.

I could let go of my pain, my worries, my sadness. Celebration!

I was free, so open.

There was peace, moments without time.

My thoughts embraced you, and I offered your sorrows to the wind, the mountains, and the sea. I asked them to lessen your agony, and help you heal your soul.

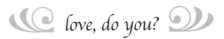 *love, do you?*

do you like the ocean

walk the beach

and when you get tired

sit and build castles

with wet sand?

I do

do you like to look far

to where the sky touches

the earth and dream

of what you might find

yonder those horizons?

I do

do you wonder some times

where heaven is

where our souls will live

and how

to find the way to there?

I do

I like to spend time

at the river

walk by fields of

waving golden grain and

watch for drifting clouds

                              do you?

I like calm nights

awe at falling stars

think about us and

where we are going

                              do you?

I like my life

harmony and peace

music and paintings

sunshine and rain

who you are

and who I am

                              yes, I do

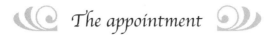

The appointment

The day was kind of ugly. All forenoon it had rained. Everything was wet. It's only the end of August, yet stiff southerly gusts push heavy clouds over the sky, ruffle trees and bushes. Strange summer, the one of 2001.

I had been early. An elderly woman in a wheelchair and a mother with her young daughter looked at me suspiciously as I entered the waiting room. It must have been my helmet or the cowboy boots that made them wonder why a guy in this bad weather had come on a motorcycle to see the doctor.

Meagan, the receptionist, sent her friendly smile my way. On my mailing list, she is convinced that my books will end up in the Hall of Fame. She introduces me to others as "our resident author." When I called this morning for an appointment she told me she would do her best.

Barely noticeably she now nodded in the direction of the corridor in back. She had managed to rearrange the schedule and squeeze me in. I would be next in line. I winked at her and had my lips silently whisper "thank you." Still, it would be a while before Angel would fetch me. I like Angi a lot. She is my hero, tirelessly comforting the doctor's fragile clientele. Angel did not want me to call her "Angi."

"I hate that name. Angel, get it? Yes?"

Killing time, I walked over to the large windows of the waiting room. I could see part of old-town Renton. The clinic had been built halfway up a fair sized hill. Its three-story front faced westerly affording a view of the new Kenworth plant. Below, through the "S-curves" meandering, the infamous I-405 crawled northwards. Most of the time it was a three-lane parking lot connecting Renton with Bellevue, the home of the truck-building giant, Paccar inc. Before I retired from my job at that company in 1994, I traveled this route many times whenever summoned to attend meetings at the corporate tower. For eight years I had been Paccar's Superfund cleanup manager at the old Pacific Car & Foundry site in town. The old firm had built railroad cars and during World War II had rolled out endlessly armored tanks for shipment to Europe. The land to the south had been seeded. It looks like a pasture now. A new truck plant spreads its buildings over the northern forty acres.

Straight west, not too far in the distance the municipal airport hid behind small houses and tall poplars. A small plane kept doing touch-and-goes. The blasted wind shook the little thing pretty hard. I thought of my Cessna and some stormy days in Alaska where I had lived during the seventies.

Bringing my mind back to the waiting room I noticed my gloves were dripping. The knees of my bulging blue jeans too were soaked. The leather jacket though was OK. It was rain-tight. My son, Misha, had given it to me last year for my birthday.

Shaking my head, I felt foolish to have taken the motorcycle. I lived only some ten minutes from the clinic. Whom was I going to impress?

I assured myself the clothes would be dry after a while and sat down next to a table neatly stacked with magazines: *Fishing, National Geographic, Better Homes and Gardens.* Near the bottom I found a copy of the *Discover* magazine. I liked to read about space, far out exploding stars, the expanding, endless universe.

Not that I understood it all, but "billions of light years" and super-tiny molecular robots fascinate me. I like to let my mind play with infinity as I perceive it to be.

The elderly lady in the wheelchair had fallen asleep. Her head, slightly tilted back, rested against a soft light blue pillow embroidered with some kind of pink blossoms. A young man, it must have been her son, came to check on her. He made sure the thin plastic tubing coming from a small, gray oxygen bottle at the back of the chair was unobstructed. For a moment he put his hands over hers she had folded in her lap. I was sure the fellow wanted to calm her, telling her everything was all right. He kissed her white hair and went over to Meagan to make sure that his mother would not miss her turn.

I felt warm about the man's kindness and said a short prayer. I am thankful I still can walk, do things, not yet needing the hands of others to help me be about. And suddenly guilt steamed up from under my leather. I worried. She had been there before I had arrived. I knew Angel would call me ahead of her. Yes. But then I thought that it would take only a minute for the doctor to tell me to keep ice on my bursitis elbow and to wear a bandage for a few days.

I had come this time only because it hurt so much more than ever before. Too, it was time to be told again that everything was OK, and elbows like mine are commonplace in people's lives. Mom and the girl were knee-deep in tic-tac-toe. All would be OK.

I dumped helmet and gloves onto the chair next to me. Thumbing through the *Discover* magazine an article got my attention.

"GALAXIES"

The page featured a full-sized picture of a disc made of stars. It looked like a huge whirlpool. Millions, maybe billions of tiny light specks cruised about a bulge in the center. I felt hot and took off my leather jacket.

A bright, yellow arrow pointed at a tiny spot, so very small, barely visible, hardly a spot at all. In the right lower corner of the page a caption said in white print that the picture depicted "our" Milky Way Galaxy. I wondered, "our?" Does Meagan or Angel own a piece of it? Who else? Wondering about that, I did not pay much attention to the finer print alongside the arrow. I assumed the thing pointed at the planet Earth, a very small place amidst the vast Milky Way.

As I began to read, it instantly sunk in that my take was off by a few billions. As always, I marveled. How more wrong could I have been? The arrow pointed at nothing less than the whole solar system with its own oblong disc measuring some ten billion miles across.

Jesus!

"Clauzie, are you ready?"

I chuckled and got up. She had warned me.

"You keep this Angi stuff up, and I will... And no, I don't care whether you think you're '*it*' or not!"

I reached for my helmet, but, still wet, it slipped from my grip, tumbled and slid like a bowling ball towards the wheelchair. On my knees I caught it just before it hit the footrest. For a moment I felt relieved. The woman did not wake, no harm done. But the situation was too funny, really. Wet gloves and magazine in one hand, the leather jacket under my arm, I kneeled on the floor and tried to get a hold of the clumsy armor. Embarrassed, I begged the Lord to make me invisible. The tic-tac-toe team could not help it. They giggled. Angel bending over covered her face with my *Health-Info-Folder*.

Meagan pretended not to see a thing. She smiled, but obviously her hands covering her mouth did not stem a coughing spell.

"Come on bike-boy, we'll weigh you…"

I mentioned 184 pounds. She grinned.

"Naked that is, yes?"

"Completely!"

Angel was teasing me, and I felt good about that. Staring at her, my grip loosened ever so slightly and my gear slipped out from under my arm. The heavy thing bounced and missed her foot by less than an inch.

Smiling she steered me towards an empty examination room, and in doing so she touched my inflamed elbow. I let out a short but audible "ouch" and picked up the hardhead for the third time.

"Oh, sorry, Clauzie. Your sore arm? Yes? O baby, I am a-sorry!"

She mistook my grinning as a forgiving gesture. Not so. Angel kept musing while she took my blood pressure. I had made sure she had the arm with the other elbow on it, the one that didn't hurt.

120 over 72.

"Nothing can excite you no more, no? 'Member, you used to come in here with your ticker pushing this mercury up close to the top. You slowing down? That I need to see!"

"How about you and me going for dinner some time soon, yes? We can talk about it then."

"Fantastic! Can I bring my boyfriend?"

I slumped. A deep breath, and then I pointed to the door.

"Angel, go away…"

While waiting for the doctor I finished my calculation. The solar system is some 30,000 light years away from the center of the Milky Way. One light year is 5,880 billion miles "long." By God, no small wonder, it was impossible for this no-spot to be there at all.

I awed at these immense dimensions and the incomprehensible expanse of space. A tiny, real tiny pinhole in that magazine page, in relation to the whole Milky Way, was large enough for the sun and all her nine planets, asteroids, comets and meteorites to slip through with ample space on the side. Wow!

"Does this hurt?"

Dr. Drie fingered the small fluid filled sack at my elbow.

I wondered why he'd asked. Of course it hurts.

"Did you bump it recently?"

"Yeah, kind of."

It would have been perfectly OK not to tell the doctor about the incident when I had "laid down" my motorbike. No, I had to spill it all. The x-ray film showed nothing unusual.

"Ice the joint and keep it bandaged for a few days. By the way, how is your book coming? Soon in the stores all over the country? Please, let me know when you have a signing in Bellevue at Borders or at B&N, yes?"

I liked this doctor a lot, trusted him, and always followed his instructions down to the dot on the "i."

Mother and daughter still were tacking. I waved at the woman in the wheelchair. She had woken up. Sonja, another nurse was pushing her along the corridor into one of those examination rooms. I blew Meagan a kiss.

"Thank you! Bye-bye!"

Half through the waiting room Angel caught up with me.

"You might need this. There is a law you know, riding a Harley without…"

"Dinner, Angi, when?"

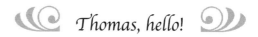 *Thomas, hello!*

It's been awhile. How are you Tommy?

Maybe I never told you. The room at the hospital in Memphis had two windows. The smaller one by your bed had a fairly wide outside ledge. One morning, my turn to be with you, I saw a raven. It had flown by a few times and then finally settled on that ledge. The bird looked at you as though it was checking if you'd be ready to go.

Of course you did not know about all this. Only the instruments said you were alive. Thomas, I knew at that moment you would not stay much longer.

And so, nowadays whenever I see a raven I think of you boarding that airplane. I remember you waving at me for the last time just before you disappeared behind the corner down at the loading ramp. Your thumbs were up, both of them. You smiled. I still can see that just like it had been only yesterday.

Sometimes I just cry, and keep driving to where I had not meant to go. Other times at stop signs I hurry a prayer asking for you to be in heaven. When I go to the mountain, ride my motorcycle on country roads alongside rivers and fields, I send my greetings to you up there.

We talked, and often you asked me to let the past go to where it belongs. I am doing that. And yet I keep wanting to change some of it, aware I cannot. Son, you do understand that, don't you?

I am getting older these days. At times I wonder if there is enough life left for me to straighten what I did bend, to caress what I have pushed away. From your vantage point it must be amusing to watch me scramble along without a clue which road leads to heaven, which one to hell.

But enough of this.

What I really wanted to tell you is that I am on my way to become a Crisis Clinic volunteer.

Get this! Tucked in between blitzing commercials disrupting the evening news, an 800 number appeared on the screen. The anchorman explained that the Crisis Clinic was in short supply of volunteers. The message could not have taken more than twenty seconds, much too short for me to realize what it meant. But for days on end the words "Crisis Clinic" kept showing up in my memory. My neighbor said,

"Naw, that's for younger people. You've done your share. You shouldn't…"

"What share? What should I not do? What do you mean by that?"

"You can't help those rejects. Don't you know about losers? They..."

And other friends of mine in between the lines let me know that I was nuts. Can you imagine? I quietly edited my mailing list. It is shorter now.

A week had gone by. I finally called Channel 4 and asked if they could give me that number.

A few days later I found the Crisis Clinic application package in my P.O. Box.

I was accepted and am in training right now. All together we are twenty people, and from all walks of life. We are a large family. I already had my first and second "listening shift"— eavesdropping on the conversation between someone who called and the phone worker.

I knew there was suffering out there—despair, anger, violence, and loneliness.

I knew there were people out there who no longer can cope, no longer can make it.

I knew there were people out there who are mentally ill, very ill.

I knew there were people out there who think about ending their lives to stop the pain.

Not that I had forgotten. But living a comfortable life had put distance between "them" and me. I, living in peace, let their misery slide into the twilight and out of focus. The urgency of their horrible reality had faded in me over time. As years passed, fewer times did I ask who would help? Who would hug the weeping mother bending over her fourteen-year-old child? Who would console the elderly woman at the grave staring at that flat stone?

I promised I would pray. And I do. Enough? Is it enough?

No.

The voices coming over our earphones are real. The events happen right now. The pain and despair is closer to home than the agonies we see unfolding on our television screens.

It is really not important to know what has gotten them into this corner of life they are calling from. They called. They want to make a change. There is no shame in asking for help. They called, that is what counts. And if we can be there for them, if only for a short while and listen, we might have helped them to better their lot.

I did not say it is an easy task. I thought with all the stuff I have in my bag, I would know how to do all this.

Yeah!

To join this team in Seattle was and is one of the best decisions I've made for some time. I found others who share compassion with each other and with those who call. I feel good belonging to this group.

So, that is what I wanted to share. I know you always lent your hand and your soul and reached out. Your music still keeps ringing in so many hearts.

Hey, if you have a moment sometime, give me a call.

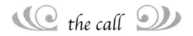 the call

"*Crisis Line…*"

you called
did not give your name
you asked me for help
my hands could not bring

you cried
I could not come to hug
you asked me for shelter
my search did not find

you despaired
I could not come to calm
you asked about tomorrow
my answer was   "It is today"

you fell silent
I could at first not understand
you asked me if giving up is ok
I begged you to stay

you ended the call
I needed more time
to ask for you to be safe

"Crisis Line…"

walking with my father

I remember looking up to him,
reaching for his hand.
father was a tall man.

on sundays we'd take the tram
to the nearby forest,
and walk between big trees
to the small lake in a quarry.

he would unstring my shoes,
and take off my stockings.
he let me go in up to my knees.

we'd eat bread and some of the
berries we picked along the way.
he liked wild strawberries.
we didn't talk much.

on the way back
we would find mushrooms.
he showed me how to pick them.

gently he put
them into the paper bag
with the berries and the leftover bread.

I carried it.

my other hand reached for his.
I am older now than he was then.
still, I need to reach
to take his hand into mine.

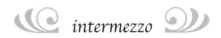 *intermezzo*

The Magnificent Microwave Anisotropy Probe Mission

The article has it that later in the year a space probe will be launched and parked one million miles yonder our planet. The Big Bang left sound waves that "jelled and froze" give or take some thirteen billion years ago. Fade echoes are still around in the form of cosmic microwaves.

The probe will measure their temperatures telling astrophysicists whether we are living in an infinite or finite universe. I am not making this up.

With this on my mind I drove to Bellevue. A beautiful day! Gail, a good friend had given to me a birthday present, a gift certificate for a full body massage at Gene Juarez's new place near the Paccar Building.

I tried to open the immense large see-through glass door. No luck. At first I feared the place was closed. Then I dared, pushed harder and the gates to pleasure came open. I entered. My insecurity index jumped off the chart beyond where it says "*MAX.*" Everybody was staring at me. Never having been in such a luxurious place I probably gave the impression of a small-town boy. My peasant-type Nikes gave me away, I know. Yes, that must have been it.

The Egyptians could have built this edifice. Wow! The drapes, the carpets, the vast space—so very beautiful! The contrast to the suburban chic outside was overwhelming, colors beyond pastel, music everywhere, soothing, melodic, barely audible. A gentle breeze hushing between the columns laden with fragrances escaping from glass-blown cruets of the mighty pharaohs tranced my mind.

Forgive me, but I cannot recall what the ceiling looked like. I was too timid to look up. The only thing confirming I still walked on this planet was the registration counter similar to the ones in very fancy hotel lobbies. Beautiful young ladies managed the counter.

My purse with cell phone dangled nonchalantly in my left hand. The collar of my beige *Members Only* windbreaker was turned up though it was 70 degrees outside. I assured myself I'd be more "in" that way. The gilded paper folder shielding the seventy-dollar gift certificate was in my breast pocket, right over my heart.

I pulled it out and shyly presented it like my first elementary school report card. Nobody looked at it.

"You have an appointment, don't you? Oh yes, at two this afternoon. One moment please."

How did she know? I was forty-five minutes early. I hate being late. My insecurity upped itself at least one more notch, approaching critical.

"Is someone helping you?" a second lady asked me. The first one tried to find my name on her monitor. She was somewhat perturbed. The computer glitched on her.

"Oh. You're Clouze."

"Claus, yes."

"Is this your first time here?"

Was she teasing me? The place had opened only yesterday. Would she have known had I lied? I've been all over the world, but I have had only one massage in Korea in the fascinating city of Pusan.

"Yes, and I am all excited about it."

Instantly depositions I had given over the years came to mind. Often my lawyer had to interrupt. "Just answer the question. Don't volunteer extraneous information, please!" Yes, sir! But at this moment I felt excited like a boy on Christmas Eve.

Now, would all this feel the same if "our" universe really were infinite? My pondering was interrupted.

"Hello Clouze, I am Jeanette. How are you? Oh good! Would you come with me, please?"

I presented my "report card." She ignored it.

"This way, please."

She had lowered her voice, close to a whisper. Again, see-through glass doors, not that tall though. She pushed them open, no sweat. Entering I was leaving "our" galaxy. I let go.

After the shower I slipped into sandals she had put out. They made me feel nomadic, like Moses walking away from the burning bush. I donned my robe "with nothing under" as Jeanette had suggested.

By the way this shower is something else. I believe a person belonging to the Sierra Club or other Earth organizations would feel guilty taking one. There is water upon water. It rains from above, squirts at your body from all four corners of the spacious stall. You might want the "rain" from above to be cool while warmer spray from other nozzles teases you. And no shower should ever be taken without steam wallowing up from hidden jets in the floor. I could not quite push the thought away that a homeless person sure would dig such an experience.

Jeanette led the way to a cavernous hall that felt like an eastern masjid.

"Please, rest. I'll bring you some ice water, yes?"

So very tenderly she whispered so as not to disturb the stillness of this dim prestigious place. The floor was of ochre sandstone probably from quarries in Italy. Silence sifted all around music in superior stereo. Angels must have been plucking the harps, so softly, sensuously, hesitating for eternities between bars.

I sank into a contoured chair. A bouquet of Arabic incense penetrated my senses. Never mind "our" galaxy…

While Jeanette retrieved the special water I dared to look up. Warm air played with thin chiffon drapes that billowed in the sway of these timeless moments. I became weightless.

"Thank you," I whispered back as the ice pinged in my glass. I hardly could hear me saying it. The room was without hurry. Nothing seemed to be more important than Clouze. I felt cozy. The robe was so soft. I wondered if God might dress like that.

There was a basin in the middle of the room. Water flowed. An ancient well? If not, mightily close to it.

Women floated by in long black gowns. Herbal aromas followed them. They could have been from a nearby convent, though their hoods were missing. There were other women too. They wore very short white skirts, black stockings and red slippers. I didn't look away, but nobody noticed.

Clutching my icy glass, I held on to it as if it were the last thin umbilical thread still connecting me with the world orbiting in distant darkness.

I felt tender hands and water streaming down over my legs. How my feet got into that bowl filled with anointed creamy liquids, I do not recall.

I opened my eyes. Another Jeanette was holding a Greek carafe. I had to read her lips. Her voice was toneless.

"Clouze, does the warmth feel comfortable to you?"

Yes, it felt damned good. I answered by shutting my eyelids.

I don't know why, sitting there in utter peace I kept thinking of those high-density, colorful clouds the Hubble scope had photographed. The light from those tall "towers of gases" millions of degrees hot, traveling billions of years to get to us... way beyond my comprehension.

What will those microwave photons tell us? Had they seen God out there at the end of infinity? Yes, I know there is no end...

"Clouze."

A third Jeanette, long black gown, no hood.

"I am sorry you had to wait so long. I am Megan, but they call me Kelly."

I used my lowest voice. Like in a trance I answered, "Hello Megan! I like your name. Are you late? This place is time-less, yes?"

"You are so sweet."

I am not quite sure. She may have really said that. To me it sounded like that. It felt good. She dried my feet, slipped on "my" sandals, and helped me up.

Magdalena? But I wasn't Him.

"Do you have any sensitive spots on your body you want me to stay away from?"

"My breasts. They hurt. My cancer treatment does that."

We entered a room, lit in amber. It smelled of wild chamo-mile and other exotic spices, probably from India or Casablanca. A raised bed stood in the middle.

"Here, Clouze, take off your robe and slip under the cover while I wait outside. OK?"

Now, I would be lying if I told you that all this did not faze me. I could not fight off some beautiful memories of slip-under-the-cover encounters. And to be honest, I did not fight it very hard, did not try at all. This was duty free time, exempt.

The bed was soft, warm, so was the feather-light cover. Yonder, I thought what a tremendous moment this would be to go home with for good, to sail away and become one of those trillions of whatevers out there.

Megan came back in and began to mold my body. I felt absolutely fabulous. A woman's hands so gently touching my head, face, my shoulders. She worked in total silence. Might heaven be this way? And I was thinking of Rodin kneading his clay into "The Thinker."

No hands had touched me, and I know, so gently ever in my whole life. I began to dream. Yes, this must be what heaven will be like.

And then it was over.

Two "hotel clerks" finally reached for my golden envelope. The atmosphere seemed appreciably cooler. They kept looking at me. Did I not zip up my fly?

Ah, how stupid of me not to think about that! The tip, of course! I searched for two tens, found two fives. Discreetly I handed over one of them. Being pretty good at reading faces, those behind that counter… naw, you don't need to know.

Yes, it really was over.

City street-reality hauled me back from those moments in heaven. I became sad. Time could have ticked a little slower, wouldn't have had to hurry that much.

Now, if NASA finds the universe not to be infinite but finite, I have problem. In what would it be finite, in infinity?

 *infinity*

Mind you, this has been written by a peasant, not by a studied man. And if you know all about God, the universe, infinity, and eternity, you might want to skip these pages and enjoy lighter prose.

I need to talk about the things I do not understand, ask questions, mull over the answers and test how far I can reach.

God has been there all the time, they say, even before that certain "drop" of matter exploded, giving birth to "our" universe and us. OK, let that go for now.

Billions of years later, we came to learn how to add numbers and to subtract from them. Some of us thought the earth to be a disc. Others had us living inside a huge ball. Let's skip Socrates and move right on to Hubble. And here is where I begin to have a hard time comprehending what I am told about the inner workings of time and space.

I know we fixed certain equations to obtain results in a lingo, we claim, man understands. To make all those answers plausible, it did take some finagling, though. We invented the concept of "infinity." We came up with the endless figure of Pi and with the natural logarithm "e" that helps us manage and use negative mathematical expressions which have no chance to ever turn positive.

By the way, you still can skip all this and go on to other pages.

OK, then.

For many years I had been convinced that infinity is a real thing. The curved legs of certain trigonometric functions change their polarity way out there in that infinity, miraculously switching plus into minus and visa versa. So, infinity must be real because changes do occur in it.

Yes? No?

But as I listened the other day to my friend Mark, it became almost clear to me that infinity does not change anything, yet only is catalytically involved in endless progressions of asymptotic processes. He said that parallel lines will always remain parallel, even in infinity.

"Well," I argued, "they could become one line, cross over or go their separate ways, way out there." I was thinking of myself standing in the middle of a railroad track between the two rails. Looking, following them with my eyes, those two rails appeared to become one as they approached the horizon. Way "before" infinity, some billions of light years in the distance? Yes, he probably is right when he claims they'd still be parallel.

It might be the place to mention that I feel most often I am the starting point, originate "things" that by their own composition eventually end up in infinity. Habitually I am looking at the "beginning" of infinity to start some time in the future. But it may be, the two parallel lines have been there already and again are speeding back into it. The process appears to me to be circular, and I have my doubts about that.

Understand, please, all this is highly theoretical since absolute parallelism is only possible on paper. I think that in reality not any value exists without a tolerance. The more so do I believe this since we have learned how to measure time in fractions of a trillionth of a second.

Mark mentioned another "thing" that made me think, though it is yonder my ability to imagine it. He stated a circle will stay a circle, even if its diameter grows infinitely large or shrinks infinitely small. OK, here is where it begins to hurt. Infinite curvature, now, how does that look? Like a straight line or an almost invisible dot?

Denny, the man who years ago gave me a job and saved me from disaster, brought up an interesting point. He suggests that the infinite curvature would appear as a real circle if viewed from an infinite distance. Ha. Could that be done? The observing instrument would have to have an "infinite x infinite" vision. And those "eyes" would need to travel a hair faster than light to escape into infinity... Oh no, let's not go there, please, no.

It's like the box within a box, inside another box, inside more and more boxes that always have sides separating an "inside" from an "outside." And no matter how many boxes—what will the "last" box be contained in? Maybe there is no "last box" at all? That is maybe why we needed to invent infinity. I must confess this metaphor works for me best if the boxes are getting larger. I can less imagine for the boxes to become smaller and smaller.

But infinity, even if it really exists, must be infinite in "something." When, where does it start? With the strike of a pen, I can make it start "right now." Yes, all I have to do is to write the equation "$1 \div 0 = ?$" I think the answer equals infinity. "They" call that result undeterminable. We can't divide any number by zero! It is not permitted. To use this equation would be an inexcusable faux pas. You see, we agree out of existence what is very tricky to explain. Yet I must ask, how long did this equation exist before I just wrote it down? May it have been around witnessing the Big Bang?

Right or wrong, as I said, I am just a peasant and think like one.

Funny, I have no problem imagining me sitting here counting for ever and ever, because I know I will not run out of numbers. I do not need infinity for this at all. Am I confused? Oh yes, I am.

Is the—or better, is "our—universe round, flat, curved, square? That question implies that round, flat, curved, square are forms conceived within a space containing them. Without that condition I am not able to distinguish between those shapes, or acknowledge the existence of any shape at all.

Whatever shape the universe may be in, it keeps expanding into that space I call "emptiness." This emptiness may contain other universes, so we are told. OK, it really doesn't matter to me. Does emptiness have an end, what is it made of, has it been there all the time, and is there something else beyond? Maybe an "infinite emptiness?" That is what matters!

I am unable to think the thought that something does not have a beginning, does not come to an end. And, on the other hand, neither could I understand if those dimensions would have a beginning and would end somewhere, some when. The torturing question remains: What was there before those dimensions began to exist? Time, too, falls into the same category. I do not want to touch the possibility that they never may have started, but always have existed.

Yes, take that first drop of matter, (and where did *it* come from?) and ask what it had been floating in, just before it blew itself up?

In God's hands?

Is that really the answer?

tumbleweeds

A little south of Wenatchee, high above the Columbia River, a gravel road crawls to the top of the desert mountains.

The switchbacks are narrow. Gusty winds chafe sage against the rocks it is growing among.

It is early, brisk. No clouds mar the wide sky. The river far below wears whitecaps, short, many. But from up here I cannot see them move.

The highway across, a narrow band with tiny cars speeding in slow motion sparkles like a chain made of silver. The long trucks look even smaller than their miniature images in toy stores.

Way below and on my side of the river a long freight train meanders towards town.

I get out of my car to catch one of those tumbleweeds that are born up here. But the rushing air takes it. The brownish colored thing somersaults down the mountain and out of my sight.

I feel good. Hissing winds, silence, blue sky, the dark waters of the river.

Life!

Much hope is dwelling in my heart. Wide are my arms stretched to embrace this moment, hold it to share with those who grieve, mourn, search for a new day.

I steer downhill, much aware of the cliff's edge the steep road tries to stay away from.

A moment in time I wish I could take with me and make last forever.

Page

The moment I took the phone, I knew it was Page.

"Whatcha doing, ma man? Tried the other night to call ya. That's a stupid message your answering machine is playing."

The nasal sound of her voice oozed from the ear-piece. Page, at one time "my Page," is a young woman who has mastered the intriguing ability to speak without really moving her lips. Her words spill into the conversation sounding similar to those emitted from handheld puppets resting on the arm of their ventriloquists.

I was tempted to answer with the same phrase my grandchildren respond with when I ask about their welfare: "Oh, nothing." But Page was not to be brushed off that easily. I knew better.

"Page, you don't want to know. It's difficult to explain, see..."

"I refuse to believe that with your IQ, you have difficulties explaining anything, unless you're floating a lie. Want me to come over and help?"

It was with her as it was with most of "my" women I had met in a bar. I seldom found myself in any position other than in a guarded mode of defense. A few telephone conversations back, I had let her squeeze a yes out of me. At the time, I had asked myself, "Why not?" Her traits had faded in my mind. My neurons did not wake up and warn me.

She had arrived in her Cadillac, black with gold plated door handles and emblem. Her lavender silk blouse, deep cut, matched the car's steering wheel cover. The golden-framed license plate said "PAGE 555."

How could I have forgotten?

"Come, give Mommy a hug, little boy."

There had been no chance for me to back away from her. I am five-foot-eleven. She reaches beyond six-foot-two. How or why we met in the first place is not relevant to this confession here.

Page's stormy hugs always hurt me. Her long drawn out "Gone with Wind" kisses, with my neighbors curiously watching, embarrassed me.

These neighbors of mine, mostly the women of course, firmly believe I belong to them. I have been told in so many words, "… Cuzz, don't you get any ideas and wander off with one of those good looking chicks." Still, it felt so good to be mothered by those neighbors of mine. They do take good care of me. During the fishing season I eat their husband's caught trout. When they harvest veggies from their gardens, I turn into the Green Giant.

That day, Page entered my domicile and within minutes had inspected my cupboards, my fridge, the living room, the bathroom, and the corner where I sleep.

I hated it; "Cuzz" should have remembered.

"I don't see how you can keep looking so good when there is no healthy food in this house of yours."

In defense I mentioned that the gene pool of my ancestors had carried flawless instructions as to my appearance and an otherwise rather pleasant aboutness.

"No other boyfriend of mine, you've met some of them, has ever been as good with bull as you are. Genes, my freakin' ass."

When she had finally left that afternoon she knew how much money I had in my checking account. She also had induced severe guilt feelings in me. Ha!

"You spent much too much money on your new stereo."

Excuse me?

She had further mentioned that my new mattress, purchased only a few weeks ago, would not be fit for her to sleep on, not even if only for one night. Was I ever glad.

"Your bedroom always was dull, boring. It still is, and now it even smells like you sleep in it. Did you ever hear of sage and citrus candles or bayberry? And you have no stove? Have you turned completely into a microwaving bum?"

Again I had to switch to defense. Annoyed about the situation, I couldn't help my hands from vibrating, unnoticeably, but definitely.

Oblivious to my indignation, Page continued her inventory. "God, I should have never left you. Just look at your hair."

During the time we "went together," she had asked me to move my stuff into her A-frame in Redondo Beach. Paying most of her bills already I found nothing wrong with it. Every morning our ritual included her "doing" my hair. She took it very seriously. A man in my position should never look like he had just crawled out of bed, and by God, for sure not in the morning!

Later that afternoon, with some effort, I guided Page back to her Cad. Kisses and hugs had been served while we were still in the mud room hidden from public view. I waved as the car soundlessly disappeared down the street.

Coming back inside my house, I felt I had not performed professionally, that I had somehow blown it—though, I couldn't quite
figure out what that "it" was.

My living room felt used. Page's Eau de France hanging
around started me snuffling, I managed to feel sorry for myself, still worrying what that "it" could have been I had blown.

Looking around, I did not recognize my house. My favorite
woolen blanket, knit by, my good friend June to keep me
comfortable during my recovery from cancer, no longer
draped my white leather armchair, but sat primly folded on
the footstool.

My two homemade sofa-pillows stood upright, propped
against the armrests of my JCPenney couch like soldiers leaning on their rifles, a most uncozy posture.

Both windows in my bedroom were wide open, straining
their hinges. The stuff I keep handy on my bathroom sink
had disappeared into the drawers of my just refurbished cabinet. The towel, precisely doubled, hung over the colorful
Plexiglas towel bar I had made. The three hooks on the bathroom door were empty of my lounging sweats and nightshirt.
I searched and found them all hanging in the closet next to
my cold-washed and air-dried shirts. The cover on my bed
showed no wrinkles. Even my bed wear could not escape
critique—my pj's needed to be more "in" or else I would
be out.

"Don't be so old-fashioned."

Again, excuse me?

Luckily at this conversation now, the right neurons jumped out of bed and came to my rescue.

"No, Page, I'm busy writing, and..."

"Same as last time, Claus! You always get an attitude. OK, don't tell me. Get a life. You are not nice..."

The click in my ear reassured me the conversation was over. Pretty sure this time her Cadillac would not be stopping at my house, driving by to check for other cars in my driveway. Maybe.

I could have told her that I was working on my neuron net. Recently its circuitry had started to perform in a somewhat iffy way, probably caused by some side effects my medicines are dragging into my system.

For instance the string of nerve cells responsible for preventing that blank stare at the opened fridge, and the question: "What is it I wanted to take out?" lately has been unable to produce satisfactory answers. Also the neuron connectors that should make sure the house key does not stay inside after the door shuts have become unreliable. Leaving the motorcycle key in the ignition when going to the market, paying for things but then not taking them with me, seem to further support my suspicion that my brain cells need to re-read their job description. Their axons and dendrites need to be spoken to.

See, now it might be more obvious why I told Page earlier that it would be difficult to explain. If I would have mentioned that I am upgrading my memory capacity (I read one can do that successfully), she might have thought that neurons exclusively have to do with sex.

Well, what can I say?

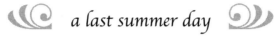 *a last summer day*

It could have been a bright day in spring, though its colors were autumnal. The sun, low and barely above the mountains to the east, did not yet share her warmth. A chilly breeze tried to sneak under my coat and down into the fingers of my gloves. To keep warm I tightened my shawl.

Steadily falling leaves carpeted the trail and made it look wider than I was used to seeing it.

Such a beautiful morning.

The colors on the trees were made in heaven, I know. So much gold and so much red, and in infinite shades between light and dark. The poplars that had scared me the other day in that fog were not gray anymore. Their gothic shapes wore tinted leaves of yellow and ochre.

Even the weedy bushes, wilting blackberry and vines on the bank across, no longer prided their bitter green. Fall there too had splattered its colors in blobs of resplendent variety. I kept walking. The sun had climbed higher into the blue sky. The light wind had stilled. I felt warmer. When I came to the small pond the trail winds around, I was stunned by what I saw. Nature, pristine and so pure held its breath. The pond's face showed not a wrinkle. The few ducks drifting left no trace on this mirror that gave birth to its shoreline on the other side.

It was an unspeakably majestic sight. And I knew that I probably not again would be witness to such an overwhelming,
magnificent moment in time.

winter

Now all this is covered with snow. The seeds autumn had shed are sleeping. Mountains, fields and fences rest from summer. Icy winds comb forlorn reeds poking through the white blanket of snow. Tree branches, laden with crystals, glitter in the cold sun. The crunch of my steps breaks the silence frozen amidst the pine trees around me. The earth is still.

My dog was anxious to come with me on my walk. All morning long his deep-brown eyes were asking me to hurry up. Now Gus is way ahead of me chasing rabbits, I guess. I hear him yelp once in a while. Could be he wants to let me to know how happy he is. I see him waiting at the fork of this invisible trail. I nod to the right, and he is gone with a howl.

Young yet, he is new in our family. We have another dog, Mady. She's black, big and strong, yet so gentle my wife lets the baby play with her. In the beginning Mady was a little jealous of young Gus, but that is better now.

I stomp on, punching through deep snow. Holes tell where I walked. Gus is right by my side, panting. He scoops snow to cool his steaming breath. Our path leads by the edge of a gigantic depression. From high up here vast views unveil surrounding mountains, valleys and sky rimmed by distant horizons. During summer, walking this trail, I always rest for a while, and let this breathtaking nature touch my soul.

Who put this vast hole there, I often wonder, made it so pristine? I catch myself imagining how immensely huge this piece of frozen water must have been. Why had the receding ice shelf left it here to die, nursed by thousands of summers? And then I muse, that block of ice can be so very proud of what it has left behind. Some time the dark water is so still, like a mirror it reflects the clouds above and the trees that line its shore. Today the lake is hidden under heavy ice. Snow-blown lifeless hills cradle it.

It's time to turn around. Gus heard me whistle. Trailed by sparkling dust he zigzags towards me. I talk to him, rub his head behind his ears. He likes that, looks up to me pushing his face into my heavy coveralls. I tell him what a good dog he is, and that I like him, and… But he cannot wait for me to finish. He's off, racing home.

The sun wants to leave. White changes into an unsure gray. All of a sudden it feels colder. Faint stars above the haze of the Columbia River twinkle at the outskirts of the universe. I think of God, my Mary, the children, and of the life we have.

Gus must have sensed what is on my mind. He comes bolting from among the trees and stands in front of me. Tilting his head a little, he seems to ask "What's up with you?"

He is so adorable when he does not understand what is going on. I'm not sure. Should I tell him that often I do not have an answer either?

Far in the distance I can see the house. Its windows spill golden light into the spreading dusk. By now Mary must be fixing dinner. She has been my best friend for so many years. I wonder if I tell her often enough that I love her?

I lean my rifle next to the door. Mady licks my face while I brush the frozen snow off my boots. Gus is slurping water. The smell of burning wood lives in our living room room. I stand by the stove and bathe my hands in its warmth.

In the kitchen, by the sink, Mary is peeling potatoes. I go over there, take the knife from her hand, the spud from the other, and give her a long hug. She leans against my shoulder. I feel her lips on my neck. And as she picks up the knife again she looks at me, tilts her head a little.

"What's up with *you?*"

 love

come and walk with me
down along the beach

I hold your hand in mine
we look for shells   for agates
and small pieces of twisted wood

the big log the tide brought in
still rocks back and forth
resting from its journey

we listen to the ocean's
waves gently splashing onto
shore   floating twigs from far away

we halt   I hold you   look into
your eyes   caress your silken hair
and then I kiss you deep and long

we keep walking into this beautiful
morning   I tell of my love and that
I want to share my life with you

will you walk with me

where are you?

thinking of you
the rain feels good

I am alone
driftwood   wet shells
gray sky   seagulls

yonder the sea is
fading into fog

I wonder what you are doing
how you fare   where you live
right now

it's been a while
since we walked this beach

these trees
have grown tall   they
remember our laughter

our spoor
tides washed away

the wind is chilly
I am cold   need to go

will I see you some day

dreaming

only for a moment

come back into my sleep and dream with me

smile

hold me like you did when you made love to me

let me caress your face   kiss your breast and

let me touch your eyes   stroke your hair

we hugged   you laughed   we begged the moment

to stay

please, be here tonight and dream with me

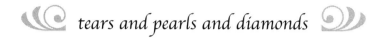 tears and pearls and diamonds

River, remember last summer, when I told you I had fallen in love with a beautiful woman? Do you? Not a year has gone by. And you have brought much water down from our mountains while I lived through beautiful dreams, a time of longing and happiness and hope.

Fall, winter and spring, and now it is summer again. I am still in love, and more so.

Wonderful, though you seem uncertain.

"My love might not be wanted…" or so I said at that time, and had asked you to bring my tears to the sea should that be so.

Yes, I do remember.

Well, you still might have to take them to the ocean, cleanse and change these salty drops into pearls and diamonds. Some day a tide, I hope, will wash them back ashore for her to find and keep.

But I do not see you cry.

— she still might fall in love with me…

Claus Hackenberger, born in 1927 in Germany, grew up near the Baltic Sea in a time of political turmoil. His parents raised him in a strict, disciplined home complemented by their strong Catholic faith. Hitler indoctrinated his young soul with fanatical, horrific ideas and taught him to kill. The Nazis made him believe that he was born to die for the Third Reich.

At the age of sixteen, Claus was plucked from school and packed off to war. During the years that followed, he went through living hell, first on the battlefield, then behind barbed wire in French slave labor camps. At Christmas in 1947, two and a half years after the war ended, he escaped and returned home, only to find his hometown in Polish hands and his family scattered. His first book, *A LONG WALK,* speaks of those years.

Nearly a decade later, Claus, his wife, and their first son arrived in America, where they became US citizens. With master's degrees in structural, mechanical, and civil engineering, Claus began a successful career. He held many positions of responsibility and prestige, his talents as an engineer and manager always in demand. Yet failed marriages, recurring alcoholism, and the death of his son Tommy deeply marred his personal life.

Still, the same indomitable spirit that would not let him succumb as a prisoner of war compelled him to find an escape from his self-imposed prison. He got well.

Claus now lives a peaceful life. He writes, sculpts, carves, and creates colorful images with brush and spatula. A recovering alcoholic of thirteen years, he is beating prostate cancer and works as a volunteer at the Crisis Clinic in Seattle, Washington. He shares his insights with thousands of people through television and radio interviews and on the internet.

"Without forgiving
I cannot make a new day,
I cannot love."